EUROPEAN
ALPINE FLOWERS
IN COLOUR

T. P. BARNEBY, B.A.Cantab.

EUROPEAN
ALPINE FLOWERS
IN COLOUR

with a foreword by
H. Gilbert-Carter
formerly Director of
Cambridge University Botanic Garden

NELSON

To
MY WIFE
who gave me the
necessary 'Time Off'
to complete
this book

THOMAS NELSON AND SONS LIMITED
36 Park Street London W1
P.O. Box 336 Apapa Lagos
P.O. Box 25012 Nairobi
77 Coffee Street San Fernando Trinidad

THOMAS NELSON (AUSTRALIA) LIMITED
597 Little Collins Street Melbourne

THOMAS NELSON AND SONS (SOUTH AFRICA) (PROPRIETARY) LIMITED
P.O. Box 9881 Johannesburg

THOMAS NELSON AND SONS (CANADA) LIMITED
81 Curlew Drive Don Mills Ontario

THOMAS NELSON AND SONS
Copewood and David Streets Camden 3, N.J.

First published 1967
© T. P. Barneby 1967

This book was designed and produced by
GEORGE RAINBIRD LIMITED
Marble Arch House 44 Edgware Road London W2

House editor: Tom Wellsted
Designer: Ronald Clark
The maps were drawn by John Flower
and the line illustrations were drawn by Ian Garrard

Printed and bound by
Jarrold & Sons Ltd, Norwich, England

Contents

Foreword

We live in an age of mechanical progress, which gives us much good. Unfortunately, it also gives us much evil, covering vast areas of our country with ugliness, noise, and bad smells, where beauty, music, and fragrance once reigned. Many are the means sensitive people use in order to escape from these ills. One of the most popular of these methods is the study of Natural History, which, before cameras and telescopes had today's excellent lenses, might have been defined as Naked Eye Biology.

Among books dealing with the identification of plants, Mr Tom Barneby's *European Alpine Flowers in Colour* will long be considered a classic. Mr Barneby is a super-excellent photographer, and his publishers are equally skilled in reproducing coloured pictures.

Tom Barneby's splendid *European Alpine Flowers in Colour* is indeed a great addition to our illustrated Floras.

H. Gilbert-Carter, M.A., M.B., Ch.B.,
*formerly Director of Cambridge University Botanic
Garden and Lecturer in Botany
Honorary Associate of the Linnean Society, London*

Acknowledgements

My thanks are due – to my mother, who first instilled in me the love of flowers; to my wife, who helped me to find some of the rarer flowers, and who gave me the 'time off' to complete the work; to Professor Humphrey Gilbert-Carter, who taught me more of the lore of flowers than did anyone else, and who has been so kind as to write a Foreword for this book. My thanks are due also to the staff of the Herbarium, British Museum of Natural History, for facilities for study at the Herbarium; to Professor P. Villaret, of Lausanne University, and Madame Villaret, who showed me some rare flowers, and generous hospitality; to the authors of all the books consulted, as listed below; and to the friendly people of the Alps, who helped me on my way. Last, but not least, I must thank Mr Tom Wellsted for the most sympathetic handling of the material placed before him.

LIST OF BOOKS CONSULTED

Binz, A. & Thommen, E. *Flore de la Suisse* (1953)

Correvon, H. *Fleurs des Champs et des Bois* (1954)

Correvon, H. *Fleurs des Eaux et des Marais* (1947)

Correvon, H. *Flore Alpine* (1958)

Dalla Fior, G. *La Nostra Flora* (1963)

Danesch, O. & E. *Nos Orchidées* (1963)

Duperrex, A. & Dougoud, R. *Orchidées d'Europe* (1955)

Favarger, Claude, & Robert, Paul-A. *Flore et Végétation des Alpes* (1958)

Fenaroli, Luigi *Flora delle Alpi* (1955)

Fournier, P. *Les Quatre Flores de France* (1961)

Gilbert-Carter, H. *Glossary of the British Flora* (1964)

Hegi, Gustav *Alpenflora* (1959)

Pitschmann, Reisigl & Schiechtl *Bilderflora der Südalpen* (1959)

Thommen, E. *Atlas de Poche de la Flore Suisse* (1961)

Introduction

THE ORIGIN, AND OBJECTS

This book began as a private collection of colour photographs of the Alpine flowers, in which I hoped to capture, and bring home with me, some small measure of their magical charm. As the collection grew, it became increasingly more difficult to name the flowers, since many of them were strange to me, so, having failed to find any book sufficiently well illustrated to help me, I was compelled to rely on the technical Floras of the Alps.

These Floras are adequate for the trained botanist, but are almost completely unintelligible to those who have not passed through what might be called the 'Visual Stage' of plant recognition, and are unable to reconstruct them, in their minds, from the technical data given. As there was no modern book on the market, which attempted to give representative pictorial coverage to the many beautiful flowers to be found in the European Alps, I decided to try, to the best of my ability, to fill the gap.

In these days of greatly improved communications, the High Alps are readily accessible to the motorist and the flower-lover, who can now enjoy the flowers, with a minimum of effort, in their own majestic setting, to the beauty of which they so lavishly contribute. Although it is true that many of the finest alpine plants do grow in inaccessible places, yet all who can spare the time to 'step aside awhile' will be surprised at how many may be found within a short walk from the main alpine highways, and it is these commoner plants which transform otherwise barren wastes into magical flower gardens.

The object of this book is, in the first place, to provide recognisable coloured pictures of as many flowers as possible, which will in most cases be sufficient to identify them, and to provide written descriptions as well, in order to assist in their identification, by drawing attention to their main characteristics, distribution, type of soil and situation, and approximate time of flowering. Secondly, it is hoped that it will help the reader to find some of the rarer flowers by showing him how to look for them, and where.

The surest aids to the discovery of rare flowers are:

1. To know the sort of situation
2. The sort of soil
3. The approximate altitude, aspect, and time of year
4. The overall distribution of the plant.

While an attempt is made in this book to give answers to these rather difficult questions, it yet remains necessary to show how those who do not have any knowledge of geology, can determine the nature of the soil. This can be done with reasonable accuracy by observing the presence or absence of the commoner lime-loving, or lime-hating plants, in the immediate area. A list of these plants is given on p. 17. There are, however, places where this rule appears to break down and both lime-loving and lime-hating plants are to be seen growing, apparently, in company. The explanation of this is that:

1. Non-limy humus often collects in hollows, even on the most limy soil, and lime-hating plants invade the area, however small it may be.
2. Limy patches may occur in non-limy areas, through the permeation of an area by waterborne lime; through lime-containing rocks and soil overlying the acid subsoil, or through outcrops of limestone within the otherwise lime-free area.

DISTRIBUTION

The presence or absence of lime-indicating plants in an area does not tell you positively what other plants of like habits you may find, because other factors may be unsuitable. It does, however, indicate rather more positively what plants you are not likely to find.

As the overall distribution of most plants is known, it is very necessary to know whether you are looking in the right area, if the plant in question has a limited habitat. It is a fact that some alpines are limited to the northern, southern, eastern or western Alps, while others are limited to even more restricted areas. Where this is so it will be indicated in the text.

ALTITUDE

The word 'alpine', when applied to plants, means in the strict sense plants whose natural habitat is at an altitude higher than the upper tree limit. Below this limit they are classified as sub-alpines, mountain, hill and plain plants, in descending order.

Whereas it is true that the strict alpine does not descend into the plains, it is also true that many plants of the lower levels do penetrate into the High Alps, and thrive there. Thus, one can see such early spring flowers as Coltsfoot and Kingcups in full flower at the tops of such passes as the Oberalp and Little St Bernard, as late as early August. Since these plants form part of the alpine scene they must be included in any book on the subject.

SITUATION

Even when the soil, distribution, and altitude are correct it is still necessary to look in the right situation. Some plants like dry situations while others like damp, wet, or boggy places. Some demand full sun, some half or full shade, while others, even more pernickety, are confined to northern, southern, eastern or western slopes or aspects, only. Again, while some plants can only survive on ground which is bare, or at most sparsely clad with other plants, others can hold their own against the strongest competition.

Other plants are parasitic, or semi-parasitic, and only exist in direct association with an individual plant, or race of plants, thus reducing their own distribution to that of the host plants. There are also a few plants referred to as Saprophytes, because they feed solely on decaying vegetable matter. They are confined to situations such as deep woodland, where their food is in good supply.

THE SEASONS

Plain-dwellers are accustomed to think of the seasons in fairly clear-cut terms as spring, summer, autumn, and winter, but in the High Alps the seasons are much less regular.

Winter lasts from the falling to the melting of the snow, when the early spring flowers impatiently push their way through its fringes as it recedes. Spring thus comes gradually and begins progressively later, as the altitude increases, and as the aspect becomes less favourable for a thaw, and may even extend into early August in some northern snow valleys. Summer quickly follows spring, and at high altitudes even tends to overtake it. Thus, traditionally spring flowers are often to be found in full bloom in company with the first flush of summer flowers. Autumn in its turn chases summer, also tending to overtake it, for time is getting short. Flowers must be produced and the seed set before the snow returns and brings such operations to a virtual standstill. There are, however, a number of spring flowers which do flower in springtime but these are mainly those plants whose upper limit is not much above the tree limit. Their spring may extend from March to mid-June, according to the altitude and aspect and yearly climatic variations. In the same way autumn may vary in duration, being brought to a close even as early as mid-September in the more unfavourable situations.

At the lower levels spring, summer, and autumn together may extend from March to October, whereas at the higher levels they may be condensed into a period as short as nine weeks, from the first or second week in July to mid-September or thereabouts.

13

An attempt is made in this book to give the approximate overall flowering periods of all the plants described, it being understood that only that portion of the whole period which is appropriate applies to any given altitude or aspect.

THE ILLUSTRATIONS

The colour photographs in this book attempt to show the flowers in their natural setting, life-size where possible, and showing their identifying characteristics. No attempt has been made to make the collection of pictures complete, since to do so, quite apart from being extremely difficult, would make the book too bulky to be readily portable, and would make it tedious to use because some of the plants are so similar that the difference would not be evident in the photographs.

In order to avoid, as far as possible, the frustration of being unable to find an illustration of a plant, particulars of many of those not shown will be found in the text.

THE TEXT

The main body of this book is, inevitably, given over to the task of describing plants.

Regretfully, I am compelled to use their Latin names, since the English, French, and German names, many of which are listed in the indices, are often misleading and unreliable. In order to assist those unaccustomed to the Latin names an Index of English Names has been prepared. In many cases there were no common English names for the plants included and it has been necessary to name them so that the index could be made comprehensive and useful to the reader. All such names are indicated by an asterisk in this index.

Full descriptions are given of all plants illustrated and the differences between similar plants emphasised. In order to do this it has been necessary to use some technical botanical terms, but these are explained in the Glossary. It is hoped thereby to make it possible, without botanical training, for anyone sufficiently interested to recognise and name the plants they find. To avoid confusing those not botanically minded, for whom this book is primarily intended, the arrangement of the Genera and the nomenclature have been kept as simple as possible, and more in line with the existing Continental Floras than with the most modern system. This has been done because, there being no current English pocket Flora of the Alps, this book is more likely to be used in conjunction with these Continental works, which do not as yet employ this new system. To bridge the gap between ancient and modern the synonyms appear in the text and in the index.

PLANT PROTECTION

In order to preserve the wild life of the Alps against the depredations of indiscriminate collectors, a large number of them have been protected by law.

In the National Parks this protection is complete for all sorts of wild life. The parks are regularly patrolled and no one is allowed to wander from the recognised pathways without an official permit. Within the limits of the parks, even the picking of an occasional flower, or the gathering of any of the edible fungi, is absolutely prohibited, under pain of severe penalties. Outside the parks certain plants are equally protected by law against being dug up or disturbed in any way, and even the indiscriminate picking of blossoms is prohibited. Were it not for these seemingly stringent regulations some of the most beautiful of the alpine flowers would soon become rare, or even extinct, and the alpine scene be robbed of one of its most outstanding features. The object of their preservation is as much to give them the chance of increasing, both themselves, and the beauty of the scenery, as it is to preserve their existence. It is a fact that the careless picking of some flowers may mean the death of the plant itself. Thus, when picking an orchid, do please remember not to pluck it roughly, but cut it neatly, leaving at least one leaf, since otherwise, every bloom you pick means one plant the less, because it will not be able to produce the new bulbil necessary for its survival.

In the case of many other plants which rely on the setting of seed for their continued survival, it is obvious that mass picking will reduce their ability to reproduce themselves efficiently, which will result in the gradual diminution of their numbers.

Finally, I make a plea to all flower-lovers that when you find them you just 'Love them, and leave them' for others to enjoy, and remember that you are only able to enjoy them now, because others have respected them in the past.

T.P.B.

List of
Protected Plants

Adonis vernalis
Anemone baldensis
Anemone narcissiflora
Anemone ranunculoides
Anemone sylvestris
Anthericum
Arnica montana
Artemisia genipii
Artemisia glacialis
Artemisia laxa
Aruncus sylvestris
Carlina acaulis
Convallaria majalis
Cyclamen europaeum
Cyclamen neapolitanum
Daphnes (all)

Dianthus alpinus
Dianthus caesius
Dianthus glacialis
Dictamnus albus
Digitalis grandiflora
Digitalis lutea
Eryngium alpinum
Fritillaria
Galanthus nivalis
Gentians (all)
Gladiolus
Hellebores (all)
Hepatica triloba
Leontopodium alpinum
Leucojum vernum

Lilium bulbiferum
Lilium bulbiferum ssp. croceum
Lilium martagon
Muscari
Orchids (all)
Paradisia
Potentilla nitida
Primulas (all)
Pulsatillas (all)
Rhododendron ferrugineum
Rhododendron hirsutum
Saxifrages (all)
Scilla bifolia
Sempervivums (all)
Silene acaulis
Valeriana celtica

Comparative List of Lime-loving and Lime-avoiding Plants

LIME-LOVING
Achillea atrata (scentless)
Androsace chamaejasme (hairy)
Anemone narcissiflora
Campanula cochlearifolia
Campanula thyrsoides
Doronicum grandiflorum
Erica carnea
Gentiana clusii
Gentiana lutea
Pedicularis foliosa
Phyteuma orbiculare
Potentilla crantzii
Primula auricula
Primula farinosa
Pulsatilla alpina
Ranunculus alpestris
Rhododendron hirsutum (hairy leaf)
Senecio doronicum
Silene acaulis
Silene vulgaris
Soldanella alpina
Trifolium badium

LIME-AVOIDING
Achillea moschata (aromatic)
Androsace obtusifolia (not noticeably hairy)
Anemone baldensis
Arnica montana
Campanula excisa
Campanula barbata
Doronicum clusii
Calluna vulgaris
Gentiana kochiana
Gentiana punctata
Pedicularis tuberosa
Phyteuma betonicifolium
Potentilla aurea
Primula viscosa
Primula hirsuta
Pulsatilla sulphurea
Ranunculus pyrenaeus
Rhododendron ferrugineum (brown-backed leaf)
Silene exscapa
Silene rupestris
Soldanella pusilla
Trifolium alpinum

The following plants also are:

LIME-LOVING
Anthyllis
Arabis
Carlina acaulis
Cirsium acaule
Digitalis grandiflora
Digitalis lutea
Dryas octopetala
Globularia cordifolia
Globularia nudicaulis
Helianthemum sp.
Hieracium villosum
Leontopodium alpinum
Linum sp.
Polygala chamaebuxus
Saponaria ocymoides

LIME-AVOIDING
Armeria alpina
Douglasia vitaliana
Eritrichium nanum
Linnaea borealis
Loiseleuria procumbens
Sempervivum sp.
Senecio carniolicus
Senecio incanus
Senecio uniflorus
Vaccinium sp.

These lists, while not being comprehensive, may be of assistance in determining the nature of the soil in any area, and give some indication as to the possibility of finding other lime-loving or lime-avoiding plants in the same locality.

Glossary

acuminate Terminating in a sharp point.

alternate Leaves originating at various angles from each other, but not from a position exactly opposite.

anther Terminal part of stamens, enclosing the pollen.

apiculate Abruptly contracting to a sharp point.

bract Leaves associated with, and an integral part of a flowerhead, and which differ often, in form and colour, from the remaining leaves.

calyx The protective envelope of sepals enclosing a flower in bud and supporting the petals when they open.

ciliate Fringed with hair-like appendages.

crenulate Edged with rounded teeth.

cordate Heart shaped.

corolla The floral envelope, inside the sepals, and composed of petals, either joined together or separate.

corymb A flowerhead in which the pedicels of the flowers arise from different points on the stem, but all attain about the same height.

cyme A flowerhead in which each blossom, other than the first open, arises from the axils of the leaves below the previous blossom. A cyme may be unilateral forming a spray, or multilateral forming a head.

deciduous Shedding its leaves in winter.

decurrent Running down below the point of origin, or of junction.

dentate Toothed at the edge.

dichotomous A stem which branches equally at each node as in a bilateral cyme.

digitate Divided like the fingers of a hand.

emarginate Concave at the tip.

entire Undivided and without teeth.

filament Part of the stamen carrying the anther.

foliose Leaf-like.

glabrous Hairless.

glaucous Bluish or greyish green.

gorge Point of entry to the corolla tube or calyx.

involucre A collarette of leaves, or bracts, enfolding a flowerhead.

keel The boat-shaped centre of the flowers of the Pea family, which enfolds the stamens and pistil.

label The lower lip of the Orchid family.

mucron A small stiff point.

node The swollen joints of stems, from which leaves and sideshoots arise. The internodes are the parts of the stem between the nodes.

pubescent Softly and sparsely downy.

obovate Egg-shaped with the big end up.

obtuse Blunt-ended.

opposite In pairs, on opposite sides of the stem.

ovate Egg-shaped, with the little end up.

palmate Composite leaves, with leaflets arising from the same point.

panicle A composite flowerhead, with branching side branches.

pedicel A stem which bears a flower or flowerhead at its tip.

perfoliate Leaves which embrace and encircle the stem.

petiole The stem of a leaf, as opposed to one of a flower.

pinnate A composite structure, divided at the edges like a feather. Pinnate leaves are either divided at the edge or have separate leaflets, in pairs, with or without a terminal leaflet. When the side divisions are also pinnate, the leaf becomes bi-pinnate, and so on.

reniform Kidney shaped.

reticulate With net-like veining.

scalloped With rounded indentations, like a scallop shell.

sepals Leaves enfolding the petals, and together forming the calyx.

sessile Stemless, either of leaves or flowers.

spatulate Spatula- or spoon-shaped, narrowing gradually towards the base.

spike A flowerhead with all the flowers arising directly from the main stem.

standard The upper, fan-shaped petal of the flowers of the Pea family.

stolon A self-rooting offshoot, arising from the stem or root of a plant.

style The part of the pistil bearing the stigma.

tomentum White or coloured felt-like down on the leaves and stems of plants.

tridentate Three-toothed.

trifid Three-lobed.

trifoliate With three leaflets.

umbel A composite flowerhead in which the pedicels arise from the same point and attain about the same height.

verticel Leaves or flowers arranged in rings around the stem.

wings Describes the lateral petals of Orchids and members of the Pea family.

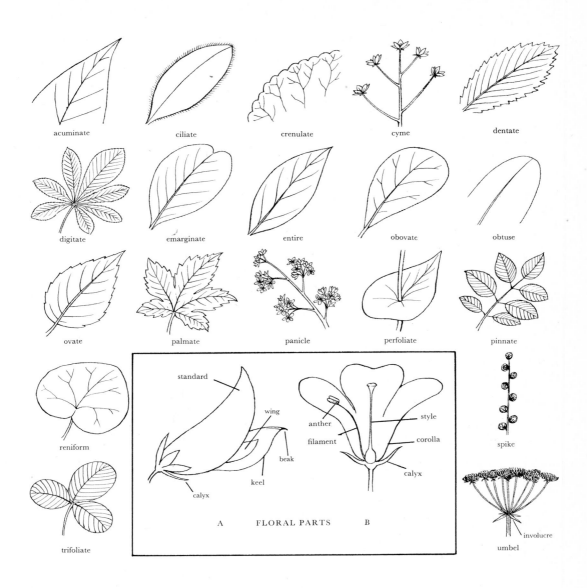

acuminate

ciliate

crenulate

cyme

dentate

digitate

emarginate

entire

obovate

obtuse

ovate

palmate

panicle

perfoliate

pinnate

reniform

standard

wing

beak

keel

calyx

anther

filament

style

corolla

calyx

spike

trifoliate

A   FLORAL PARTS   B

involucre

umbel

19

Map of the French Alps

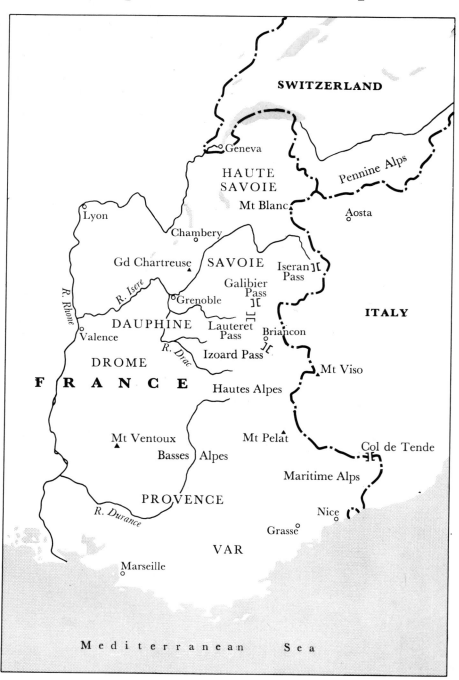

Map of Switzerland

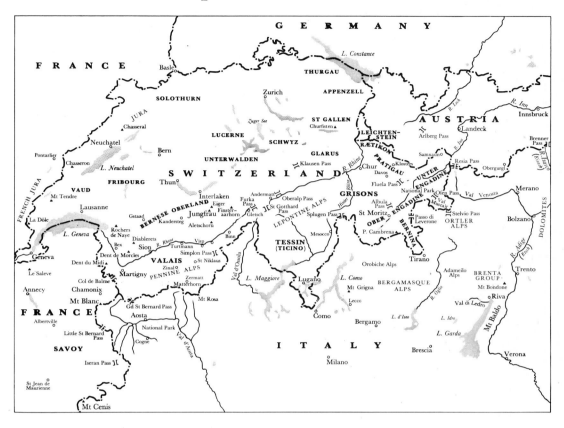

Orchid Identification Drawings

Ophrys insectifera

Ophrys apifera

Ophrys fuciflora

Ophrys aranifera

Cypripedium calceolus

Orchis militaris

Orchis ustulata

Aceras anthropophorum

Orchis morio

Orchis purpurea

Orchis simia

Orchis tridentata

Orchis globosa

Orchis incarnata

Orchis latifolia

Orchis maculata

Orchis mascula

Orchis laxiflora

Orchis provincialis

Orchis palustris

Orchis traunsteineri

Orchis sambucina

Orchis pallens

Himantoglossum hircinum

Platanthera bifolia

Platanthera chlorantha

Anacamptis pyramidalis

Chamorchis alpina

Coeloglossum viride

Herminium monorchis

Leucorchis albida

Gymnadenia conopsea

Gymnadenia odoratissima

Nigritella nigra

Nigritella rubra

Epipactis palustris

Epipactis latifolia

Epipactis atropurpurea

Epipactis microphylla

Epipactis purpurata

Listera ovata

Listera cordata

Spiranthes-summer

Spiranthes-autumn

Goodyera repens

Corallorhiza trifida

Neottia nidus-avis

Epipogium aphyllum

THE PLATES

Plate 1

LILIACEAE

1 *Tofieldia calyculata* L.
Tofield's Asphodel

4–12 ins. Leaves Iris-like. Stems slender, bearing dense cylindrical heads of small, greenish-yellow flowers. Widespread, in damp places, up to 5500 ft. 6–9.

2 *Veratrum album* L.
Langwort,
White False Hellebore

25–56 ins. Stems densely leafy. Leaves large, oval, deeply wrinkled, and rather similar to those of the Yellow Gentian, *Gentiana lutea*, Plate 62, but arranged alternately, instead of opposite. Flowers greenish-white, borne in a tall, dense, usually branching, spike. Widespread, in damp places up to over 7000 ft. 6–8.

Veratrum nigrum L.
Black False Hellebore

20–60 ins. Similar to the above, but with blackish-brown flowers, and, in the Alps, confined to the south and east. Rare in the Maritime Alps, and in Switzerland, only in the Tessin. Between 4000–5000 ft, approximately. 6–8. Rare.

3 *Asphodelus albus* Mill.
White Asphodel

20–48 ins. Leaves tall, sword-shaped. Flowers white, or white, washed rose, borne in a tall, dense spike. Rare in Switzerland, but commoner in the west and south (Lauteret Pass, Mt Baldo), between 3000–6000 ft. 5–7.

4 *Paradisia liliastrum* L.
St Bruno's Lily

12–20 ins. This beautiful Lily is plentiful, in places, both in the Swiss and the French Alps. Perhaps the finest colony is to be found on the Lauteret Pass. 6–7.

5 *Anthericum liliago* L.
St Bernard's Lily

12–20 ins. Flowers starry, white, borne in a loose spike. Style ascendant. Locally abundant, on limy soil, in the warmer sub-alpine valleys, up to over 5000 ft. 6–7.

6 *Anthericum ramosum* L.
Branched Anthericum

12–32 ins. Similar to the above, but with smaller, starry, white flowers, straight style, and branching stem. Widespread, on dry limestone slopes, up to 6000 ft. 6–7.

1

2

3

4

5

6

Plate 2

LILIACEAE *(continued)*

1   *Lilium bulbiferum* L.
Orange Lily

12–36 ins. Flowers large, erect, 1–5 per stem, bright orange flecked brown. Small bulbils are borne in the axils of the leaves. This magnificent plant is a native of the eastern limestone Alps, the Dolomites, the Italian Alps, and in Switzerland, only in the Engadine. Local, up to nearly 5000 ft. 6–7.

2   ssp. *croceum* L.
L. croceum (Chaix) Arcang.

12–36 ins. A sub-species of the above, with flowers reddish-orange, paler in the throat, and without bulbils in the axils of the leaves. Local, in the western Alps and in the Jura. 6–7.

3   *Lilium martagon* L.
Martagon Lily, Turk's-cap Lily

12–36 ins. Stem leaves verticillate. Flowers nodding, dull rose, spotted purple, and with petals much reflexed, borne in an impressive terminal spike. Widespread, in limestone woods, and meadows, up to nearly 7000 ft. 7–8.

4   *Fritillaria meleagris* L.
Snake's-head Fritillary

8–16 ins. Stems with one or two linear leaves. Flowers large, solitary, drooping, chequered purple and white. Marshy meadows, up to 2400 ft. Local. 4–5.

5   *Fritillaria involucrata* All.
Collared Snake's-head Fritillary

8–16 ins. Leaves linear, verticillate, the uppermost ones forming a sort of false involucre around the flower. Flowers more greenish, or yellowish, than above. Rocky woods and scrubland, between 1500–4500 ft, mainly in the Maritime Alps. Local. 4–5.

6   *Gagea fistulosa* Ramond
Yellow Gagea
G. liottardii Schultes

4–6 ins. Ground leaves linear, semi-cylindrical in section. Stem leaves 2, broad and unequal in size. Flowers golden-yellow, borne 1–5 per stem. Local in damp meadows, often near cowsheds, between 5400–8400 ft. 5–7.

1

2

3

4

5

6

Plate 3

LILIACEAE (*continued*)

1 *Lloydia serotina* L.
Mountain Spiderwort

2-4 ins. Base leaves narrowly linear. Stem leaves lanceolate. Flowers white, streaked rose, borne singly as a rule. Local, in rocky, lime-free meadows, from 5700–9300 ft. 6–7.

2 *Colchicum autumnale* L.
Autumn Crocus, Meadow Saffron

4–8 ins. Rosy-lilac flowers appear in the autumn, forming sheets of colour in the damp meadows, from the plains, up to 6000 ft. The leaves and seedpods may be seen in the meadows during the spring. 8–10.

Colchicum alpinum DC.
Alpine Autumn Crocus

Similar to the above, but smaller, with narrower petals, and with style straight, below the small, capitate, stigma. In *C. autumnale*, the style is thickened and arching at the tip, and the stigma is decurrent. Local, in mountain meadows, up to 6000 ft. 7–8.

3 *Allium victoriale* L.
Stag's Garlic

12–24 ins. Stems with, usually, two broadly lanceolate leaves. Flowers greenish-white, in a dense, spherical, head. Local, in rocky, bushy places, from 4500–6600 ft. 6–7.

Allium schoenoprasum L.
Chives

6–12 ins. The well-known garden herb. Flowers rose. Stamens shorter than petals. Local, in damp meadows. 5–8. From 1500–6800 ft.

4 *Allium sibiricum* Garcke

A very large and robust form of *A. schoenoprasum*, seen occasionally.

5 *Allium pulchellum* G. Don
Elegant Garlic

12–24 ins. Leaves narrowly linear. Flowerheads without bulbils. Flowers rosy-purple, with stamens longer than the petals. South-western and southern Alps. Rare in Switzerland, and from 1200–3600 ft. 7.

6 *Allium insubricum* Boiss. & Reut.
Southern Garlic

8–18 ins. Leaves grey-green. Flowerheads always drooping, with a few, large, rosy-lilac, flowers. Local, in the Italian Alps, between L. Como and Corna Blacca, and only on limestone, between 5000–6000 ft. 6–8.

1

2

3

4

5

6

Plate 4

LILIACEAE (*continued*)

1 *Ornithogalum umbellatum* L.
Star of Bethlehem

4–12 ins. Flowers white, greenish outside and borne in an umbel-like corymb. Widespread, but local, on banks, and in meadows, up to 4500 ft. 4–5.

2 *Ornithogalum pyrenaicum* L.
Spiked Star of Bethlehem, Bath or **French Asparagus**

20–30 ins. Flowers yellowish-green, edged white, and borne in a very long, narrow spike. The leaves die before the end of the flowering period. Local, in meadows, in the western and north-western Alps, up to 3000 ft. 5–6.

3 *Streptopus amplexifolius* L.
Wood Streptopus
S. distortus Michx.

8–40 ins. Stem branching, and arching at the tip. Leaves oval-acuminate. Flowers whitish, borne singly, on thread-like pedicels, arising from the axils of the leaves, but turning under the leaf, along its mid-rib, where it is jointed so that the flowers seem to hang from, and be attached to, the mid-rib. This curious plant is not often seen, as it grows mainly in damp mountain woods and Alder thickets. It may be found in the Jura, Vaud, Valais (Simplon), Grisons (Bernina) and elsewhere, from 2400–6900 ft. Local 5–8.

4 *Polygonatum verticillatum* L.
Whorled Solomon's Seal

12–24 ins. Stem erect. Leaves lanceolate, arranged in verticels of 4–5 leaves. Flowers borne verticillate, 1–3 per pedicel, in the axils of the leaves. Widespread in mountain woods, from 1500–6900 ft. 5–7.

5 *Polygonatum officinale* All.
Lesser or **Angular Solomon's Seal**
P. vulgare Desf.,
P. odoratum (Mill.) Druce

6–16 ins. Stem angular, arching. Leaves large, oval, alternate. Flowers large, white, tipped green, borne singly, or 1–3, in the axils of the leaves. Widespread, in rocky places, up to 6000 ft, and mainly on limestone. 5–6.

6 *Polygonatum multiflorum* L.
Common Solomon's Seal, David's Harp

12–32 ins. Stem cylindrical, arching. Leaves alternate, smaller than in the above. Flowers small, white, unscented, borne, usually, 3–5 in the axils of the leaves. Widespread, in woods and by the wayside, up to 3600 ft. 4–6.

Plate 5

LILIACEAE (*continued*)

1 *Scilla bifolia* L.
Two-leaved Squill

4–10 ins. Leaves, as a rule, 2, hence the name. Flowers blue, rarely rose, or white. Open woods, and damp meadows, up to 4500 ft. Locally abundant, March to mid-June, as the snow recedes.

2 *Scilla italica* L.
Italian Squill

Leaves narrow, 3–6 in number. Flowers blue, numerous in a dense, conical, spike. Maritime, and Ligurian Alps (Col de Tende). 4–5.

3 *Muscari atlanticum* Boiss. & Reut.
Grape Hyacinth
M. racemosum auct.

4–12 ins. Leaves very narrow, and often longer than the flower stem. Flowers very dark blue, borne in a densely compact ovoid head. Locally common, up to about 5000 ft. 3–5.

4 *Muscari comosum* L.
Tassel Hyacinth

12–28 ins. Stem surmounted by a plume of amethyst-blue, sterile, flowers, on long pedicels. Fertile flowers are borne on the lower part of the stem, and are brownish-green in colour. Locally abundant in the west and south. Rare or absent, elsewhere. Up to 4000 ft. 4–7.

5 *Aphyllanthes monspeliensis* L.
Blue Aphyllanthes

4–10 ins. Leaves reduced to scales. Stems serried, rush-like, slender, grey-green. Flowers bright blue, borne 1–3, at the tips of the stems. Dry, stony places in the south and west, up to 3000 ft. 4–7.

6 *Paris quadrifolia* L.
Herb Paris, True Love

10–20 ins. Stem with, as a rule, 4 leaves, arranged in a verticel. The specimen illustrated has 5 leaves. Flowers borne singly, are greenish in colour and composed of 4 sepals, and 4 petals, arranged as crosses. Berries blue-black. Widespread, in mountain woods, up to 6000 ft. 4–5.

1

2

3

4

5

6

Plate 6

LILIACEAE (*continued*)

1 *Maianthemum bifolium* (L.) Schmidt
May Lily
Smilacina bifolia Desf.

4–10 ins. Stem carrying 2 oval-cordate leaves. Flowers small, white, borne in a compact, plumose spike. Scented. Berry red, when ripe. Widespread in woods, up to over 6000 ft. 4–6, or even 7.

2 *Convallaria majalis* L.
Lily of the Valley

Widespread in the woods of the Alps and Jura, up to over 6000 ft. 5–7.

3 *Tulipa australis* Link
Southern Tulip

6–12 ins. Flowers golden-yellow, with outer petals suffused with red outside. Local, in the southern Alps, up to 6000 ft. 4–7.

AMARYLLIDACEAE

4 *Narcissus pseudonarcissus* L.
Wild Daffodil

Common in places. Mountain meadows, up to over 6000 ft. 3–6.

5 *Narcissus exsertus* Haworth
Narrow-leaved Narcissus

12–24 ins. Similar to *N. poeticus*, which is not wild in the Alps, but with stamens protruding from the tube of the corolla. Common in places up to over 6000 ft. 5–6.

Leucojum vernum L.
Spring Snowflake
6 var. *carpathicum*

6–12 ins. Flowers large, white, drooping, borne singly, as a rule. Petals green tipped. Locally abundant, on limy soil, up to 4500 ft. 2–4.
Has yellow tipped petals.

1

2

3

4

5

6

Plate 7

IRIDACEAE

1 *Crocus albiflorus* Kit.
Wild Crocus
C. purpureus Weston,
C. vernus Wulfen

Flowers white, or lilac. Blossoms as the snow recedes. Common in places, where it carpets the alpine meadows, up to nearly 7000 ft. 3–6.

2 *Gladiolus segetum* Ker-Gawl.
Cornfield Gladiolus

20–30 ins. Flowers purple, with upper petals longer and wider than the others. Anthers as long or longer than their filaments. Mainly in cultivated ground, and not at the higher elevations. 5–6.

Gladiolus palustris Gaudin.
Marsh Gladiolus

8–20 ins. Flowers smaller than the above, and borne 2–5, on slender stems. Anthers shorter than their filaments. Local, in meadows, up to over 2000 ft. 5–7.

ORCHIDACEAE

Cypripedium calceolus L.
Lady's Slipper

Leaves large, with prominent nerves. Flowers large, usually solitary, with reddish-brown, spirally curled petals, and inflated yellow label. This beautiful plant is becoming increasingly rare, owing to the depredations of vandals, but may still be found in out-of-the-way places, in open woods, and scrubland, on limestone, mainly in mountainous districts, but not above 4000 ft. 5–7. See page 22.

3 *Ophrys insectifera* L.
Fly Orchid
O. muscifera Huds.

6–16 ins. Flowers small, widely spaced, on slender, erect stems. Outer divisions of flower greenish. Inner divisions brown and velvety. Label nearly flat, velvety, purplish-brown, with a blue central patch, narrow side lobes and forked central lobe. Widespread on dry limestone slopes, where it may be often found in company with other Orchids, such as *Orchis militaris*. 5–6. See page 22.

4 *Ophrys aranifera* Huds.
Early Spider Orchid
O. sphegodes Mill.

ssp. *atrata* Lindl.

6–12 ins. Flowers with outer divisions greenish. Inner divisions linear, blunt-ended, also greenish. Label slightly convex, brownish-purple, edged yellow, and with irregular, bluish, 'H'-shaped, central patch. No terminal appendage, as a rule. To be found in similar situations as *O. muscifera* but less common and earlier flowering. Local, up to 2400 ft. 4–6. See page 22.
The sub-species, *atrata*, has no yellow border to the label, and the inner divisions of the flower are edged with red. The flowers are also larger, and the flowering period later. Southern Alps.

5 *Ophrys fuciflora* Crantz
Late Spider Orchid
O. arachnites Scop.

Flowers with outer divisions rose, or white and green nerved. Inner divisions shortly triangular and velvety, rose. Label entire convex, purplish-brown, edged yellow, and with a bluish central patch, irregularly outlined with yellow. The label is terminated by a 3-lobed appendage, pointing to the front. Fairly frequently found in company with the Fly Orchid and up to 4000 ft. 5–6. See page 22.

Ophrys apifera Huds.
Bee Orchid

O. apifera and the other European species of *Ophrys* are to be found at lower altitudes. See page 22.

6 *Orchis globosa* L.
Round-headed Orchid
Traunsteinera globosa Rchb.

10–12 ins. Leaves pointed, the upper ones very small. Flowerhead globular. Flowers rose. Petals with spatulate tips, inturning at first to form a hood, but later wide open. Spur descendant, about half as long as ovary. Widespread, on mountain meadows, from 2700–7800 ft. 6–8. See page 22.

1

2

3

4

5

6

Plate 8

ORCHIDACEAE (*continued*)

ORCHIDS WITH ALL DIVISIONS, EXCEPT THE LABEL, INTURNING, TO FORM A HOOD

1   *Orchis morio* L.
Green-winged Orchid

4–12 ins. Flowerhead loose, few flowered. Flower divisions purple, or violet, the outer ones striped green outside. Label with middle lobe blunt, or divided. Spur horizontal, or ascendant. Common. Damp meadows, up to over 5000 ft. 4–6. See page 22.

Orchis papilionacea L.
Butterfly Orchid

4–16 ins. Stem with up to 10 flowers. Petals and sepals bright rose, pointed, inturning to form a hood. Label rounded, entire, violet-rose, veined darker. Spur conical, descendant, shorter than the ovary. Bracts washed rose, longer than the ovary. Mainly to be found in the South of France (Var, Estérel, Maritime Alps), and in Italy (L. Como area). In Switzerland, only in the South Tessin. Local, up to about 1200 ft. 3–5. See page 22.

Orchis coriophora L.
Bug Orchid

8–16 ins. Stem with many flowers, arranged compactly, in a conical head. Petals and sepals joined at the base, inturning to form a hood, and reddish-brown in colour. Label with central lobe entire, longer than the 2 side lobes, reddish-brown, washed green at the tips. Local, in poor, damp, meadows, up to 5400 ft. 4–6. See page 22.

Orchis tridentata Scop.
Toothed Orchid

8–16 ins. Flowers closely serried, in a tightly-rounded head. Hood rose. Label pale rose, spotted purple, with 3 lobes, the central one being longer, and tridentate at the tip. Spur more than half as long as the ovary. Confined to the South of Europe, and to the Tessin, and South Grisons, in Switzerland, up to 4200 ft. 3–5. See page 22.

2   *Orchis ustulata* L.
Burnt-tipped or
Dwarf Orchid

4–14 ins. Flowers small, in a dense cylindrical spike. Hood blackish-purple. Label white, spotted purple. Spur less than half as long as the ovary. Locally abundant, in limestone meadows, up to 6000 ft. 5–7. See page 22.

3   *Orchis purpurea* Huds.
Lady Orchid

12–24 ins. Flowers large, in a dense spike. Hood blackish-purple. Label pale rose to white, with narrow side lobes, and broad, obcordate, central lobe. Local, in meadows, and clearings, up to 2000 ft. 5. See page 22.

4   *Orchis militaris* L.
Soldier Orchid

10–18 ins. Hood pointed, pale rosy-mauve, paler then label. Label rose, spotted purple, with 2 lateral lobes and 2 widely divergent terminal lobes between which is a small tooth. Widespread on dry limy meadows, and slopes, up to over 5000 ft. 5–6. See page 22.

Orchis simia Lam.
Monkey Orchid

Rather similar to the Soldier Orchid, but flowerhead more globular, and upper flowers opening before the lower ones, which is an unusual feature. The lobes of the label are all about the same width, very narrow, long and markedly upturned at their tips. Much less common than the above, but occasionally to be found in company with it, in more shady positions, and at lower altitudes. 5–6. See page 22.

ORCHIDS WITH OUTSIDE DIVISIONS HORIZONTAL, OR ERECT

SPUR HORIZONTAL, OR ASCENDANT

5   *Orchis pallens* L.
Pale Orchid

8–16 ins. Flower pale yellow, with label terminated by 3 rounded lobes. Spur barely as long as the ovary. Local, in mountain meadows (Val d'Abondance, in Savoy), between 1500–6000 ft. 4–6. See page 22.

6   *Orchis provincialis* Balb.
Provençal Orchid

8–12 ins. Leaves spotted purple-brown. Flowers pale, or bright yellow, with slightly darker label, and borne in a loose spike. Spur shorter than the ovary. Local in the southern Alps, up to 3000 ft. 4–5. See page 22.

1   2   3

4   5   6

Plate 9

ORCHIDACEAE (*continued*)

ORCHIDS WITH OUTSIDE DIVISIONS HORIZONTAL, OR ASCENDANT

SPUR HORIZONTAL, OR ASCENDANT

1   *Orchis mascula* L.
Early Purple Orchid

6–16 ins. Flowers in loose spike, lengthening with age. Label spade-shaped, with wide lateral lobes, deeply divided from the longer, narrower, 2-lobed, central lobe. Flowers purple, with pale streak down middle of label, which is dotted with purple papillae. Widespread, in woods, and damp meadows, up to about 7000 ft. 4–6. See page 22.

Orchis palustris Jacq.
Bog Orchid

12–24 ins. Leaves linear-lanceolate, tapering from the base. Flowers clear violet-purple. Label 3-lobed, with central lobe at least as long as the side lobes, and either entire, or divided at the tip. The flowers are borne in a loose, few-flowered, spike. Prefers a limy soil. Uncommon, on marshy ground, up to 1500 ft. 6–7. See page 22.

Orchis laxiflora Lam.
Loose-flowered Orchid

12–20 ins. Flowers purple, borne loosely, 6–20 on a slender stem. Label with 2 wide lateral lobes, which are crenulate at the edge, and much reduced central lobe. It thus appears to be obcordate. Lime avoiding. Marshy ground, up to 3600 ft. 5–6. See page 22.

SPUR DESCENDANT

2   *Orchis sambucina* L.
Elder-scented Orchid

Flowerhead broad and compact, with long bracts between the flowers, which are yellow with a purple throat, or purple with a yellow throat. Spur large, at least as long as the ovary. Local but sometimes seen in huge drifts as on the Simplon Pass, where the two colours are more or less equally in evidence. Meadows and clearings. 1500–6000 ft. 5–6. See page 22.

Dactylorhiza: the following three Orchids, *O. incarnata*, *O. maculata* and *O. latifolia*, are now grouped, together with others, under the name of *Dactylorhiza*, as, owing to their variability of form, they were very difficult of determination. Other Orchids, grouped under this heading include *O. traunsteineri*, *O. purpurella* and *O. praetermissa*, of which only the first occurs in the Alps.

3   *Orchis incarnata* L.
Marsh Orchid
Dactylorhiza incarnata (L.) Soó, Dactylorchis incarnata (L.) Vermeul., O. strictifolia Opiz

8–24 ins. Leaves unspotted, tapering from the base, and with apex hooded. Flowers flesh-pink to rosy-violet, in a compact spike, intermingled with large bracts. Label entire, or faintly lobed. Widespread in marshy places, up to over 6000 ft. 5–6. See page 22.

4   *Orchis fuchsii* Druce
Common Spotted Orchid
Dactylorhiza fuchsii (Druce) Soó, Dactylorchis fuchsii (Druce) Vermeul.

8–24 ins. Leaves spotted brown, decreasing in size up the stem and not reaching the flowerhead. Flower spike dense. Flowers rose, or lilac, streaked and spotted purple. Label 3-lobed. Stem not hollow. Widespread, in damp places up to 6000 ft. 5–7.

5   *Orchis latifolia* L.
Broad-leaved Orchid
Dactylorhiza latifolia auct.

6–18 ins. Leaves oblong-oboval, often spotted brown. Flower spike dense. Flowers purple-violet, with darker markings. Label broader than long, with wide lateral lobes, and small, pointed, central lobe. Marshy meadows up to about 7000 ft. 5–7. See page 22.

Orchis traunsteineri Saut.
Traunsteiner's Orchid
Dactylorhiza traunsteineri (Saut.) Soó, Dactylorchis traunsteineri (Saut.) Vermeul.

6–16 ins. Stem solid, or only faintly hollowed. Leaves not reaching the flowerhead. Flowers very variable, purple, spotted and streaked darker, are borne 6–10 per stem. Label faintly 3-lobed. Leaves spotted brown. Widely distributed, but uncommon, on marshy ground, up to over 5000 ft. 6–8. See page 22.

6   *Anacamptis pyramidalis* L.
Pyramidal Orchid
Orchis pyramidalis L.

10–20 ins. Leaves lanceolate, the upper ones almost linear. Flowerhead densely pyramidal, and composed of small, bright rose, to carmine, flowers. Label 3-lobed. Spur thread-like, longer than ovary. Locally abundant in damp limestone meadows, up to about 6000 ft. 6–7. See page 22.

1

2

3

4

5

6

Plate 10

ORCHIDACEAE (*continued*)

1 *Aceras anthropophorum* L.
Man Orchid

8–24 ins. Flowers yellow, edged purple, in a long, very narrow spike. Upper divisions inturning to form a hood. Label with 4 linear lobes, hanging vertical. Locally abundant, on dry limestone slopes, often in company with the Soldier Orchid. Rare in the Alps, but plentiful in the Jura, and parts of France. Found up to 4500 ft. 5–6. See page 22.

2 *Himantoglossum hircinum* (L.) Spreng.
Lizard Orchid
Loroglossum hircinum Rich., Orchis hircina (L.) Crantz

12–28 ins. Flower spike very large. Upper divisions of the flower inturning to form hood. Label with narrow side lobes, and very long, spirally twisted, central lobe. Flowers greenish, spotted reddish, and with an odour of Vanilla or some say, 'Billy-goat'. Local, on dry limestone banks up to 2400 ft. 5–6. See page 22.

3 *Coeloglossum viride* L.
Frog Orchid

4–10 ins. Leaves oval. Flowers greenish, often washed purple. Bracts longer than flowers. Upper divisions of flowers forming a hood. Label parallel sided, divided at the tip into 2 lobes, with a small tooth in between. Poor meadows, up to about 7000 ft. Common. 5–8. See page 22.

Chamorchis alpina L.
Small Alpine Orchid

2–4 ins. Leaves narrow, often as tall as the flower stem. Flowerhead carries a few greenish-yellow to reddish-brown flowers. Label entire, tongue-shaped. Owing to its smallness and dullness of colour, this Orchid is rather difficult to find. Rare, on high alpine meadows, from about 5000–8000 ft. 7–8. See page 22.

Herminium monorchis L.
Musk Orchid

4–12 ins. Flowers small, greenish-yellow, borne on slender stems. Label with 3 narrow lobes. Odour of Musk. Uncommon, on dry limestone meadows up to about 5000 ft. 5–7. See page 22.

4 *Serapias vomeracea* Burm.
Long-petalled Serapias
S. pseudocordigera Moric.

8–20 ins. Bracts and hood violet-fawn. Upper divisions joined, almost to their tips, to form a hood. Label with 2 lateral lobes, partly concealed by the hood and a long, tongue-shaped central lobe, fawn-red in colour, hairy on top and with 2, almost parallel, longitudinal ridges, at the base. *S. vomeracea* is the only Serapias to attain the alpine regions. Shady places, up to 3000 ft. 4–6.

5 *Nigritella nigra* L.
Black Vanilla Orchid

4–10 ins. Leaves linear, erect. Flowers purplish-black, in a dense, conical spike, which later becomes ovoid. Flowers occasionally red, or white. Divisions of flowers narrow, pointed, the inner ones narrower than the outer. Label triangular, pointing up, instead of down. Widespread in alpine meadows, between 3000–7000 ft. 6–8. See page 22.

var. *flava*

Has yellow, tinged reddish-black flowers. Occurs occasionally.

6 *Nigritella rubra* Richter
Red Vanilla Orchid
N. miniata Crantz

Similar to the above, but with oval flowerhead, and red flowers. Label longer, more pointed, and with its base inturning to cover the organs of reproduction. Found in the same situations as the above, but much less common, except in the south and east Alps. Flowering period commences about 2 weeks earlier. See page 22.

1

2

3

4

5

6

Plate 11

ORCHIDACEAE (continued)

1 *Leucorchis albida* E. Mey
Small White Orchid
Gymnadenia albida Rich.,
Habenaria albida Sw.

4–10 ins. Flowers small, greenish-white, borne on a slender, compact, spike. Label deeply 3-lobed. Other divisions of flower inturning to form a hood. Alpine meadows, from 2400–over 7000 ft. 6–7. See page 22.

2 *Gymnadenia conopsea* (L.) R.Br.
Scented Orchid
Orchis conopsea L.,
Habenaria conopsea (L.)
Benth.

12–24 ins. Leaves lanceolate. Flowers rosy-lilac, with outer divisions out-spread, the lateral ones descendant. Strongly scented. Label 3-lobed, wider than long. Spur threadlike, descendant, much longer than the ovary. Damp mountain meadows, up to 7000 ft. 6–7. See page 22.

3 *Gymnadenia odoratissima* (L.)
Rich.
Fragrant Orchid

6–16 ins. Rather similar to the above, but with smaller, narrower heads of flowers. Flowers small with lateral divisions horizontal, and label slightly longer than wide. Spur descendant, shorter than the ovary. Strongly vanilla scented. Found in similar situations as *G. conopsea*, but not above 5000 ft and less common. 6–7. See page 22.

4 *Cephalanthera rubra* (L.) Rich.
Red Helleborine

8–20 ins. Leaves lanceolate. Flowers ascendant, bright rose, with all divisions pointed at their tips, borne in a loose, few-flowered spike. Local in light limestone woods, up to over 5000 ft. 6–7.

5 *Cephalanthera alba* Crantz
White Helleborine
C. damasonium Mill.,
C. pallens Rich.,
C. latifolia Janchen

10–24 ins. Leaves oblong-oval, pointed. Bracts longer than ovary. Flowers creamy white. Label with orange gorge. Common in places. Limestone woods, up to over 3000 ft. 6.

6 *Cephalanthera longifolia* L.
Long-leaved White Helleborine
C. ensifolia (Schmidt) Rich.

8–20 ins. Leaves sword-shaped, longer than the flowerhead. Bracts shorter than the ovary. Flowers pure white. Similar situations as the above, but up to over 4000 ft. 5–6.

1   2   3

4   5   6

Plate 12

ORCHIDACEAE (continued)

1 *Platanthera bifolia* (L.) Rich.
Lesser Butterfly Orchid
Habenaria bifolia L.,
Orchis bifolia L.

8–20 ins. Bears 2 leaves at ground-level. Flowers white, very sweetly scented, and borne in a slender spike. Spur long, tapering to a fine point. Anthers close together, and parallel. Widespread in light woods, and meadows, up to over 6000 ft. 5–7. See page 22.

2 *Platanthera chlorantha* Custer
Butterfly Orchid
Habenaria chlorantha Bab.

8–20 ins. Flowers rather larger, unscented, greenish-white. Spur long, enlarged at the tip. Anthers widely divergent at the base. Similar situations as the above, but not over 3600 ft. 5–7. See page 22.

3 *Limodorum abortivum* L.
Leafless Limodorum

12–32 ins. A leafless saprophyte (living on decaying vegetable matter). Stem blackish-purple, scaly. Flowers large, greyish-violet, tinted rich violet, borne in a long, loose spike. Flowers open only in favourable seasons. Open woods, and scrubland, most frequently near Scots Pines. Rare. 5–6.

4 *Epipactis palustris* (Miller) Crantz
Marsh Helleborine

12–20 ins. Leaves oblong-lanceolate. Flowers drooping. Outside divisions brownish, inner ones white. Label long, white, tinged yellow, and with front section narrowly joined to the base. Boggy places up to 4500 ft. Local. 6–7. See page 22.

5 *Epipactis atropurpurea* Raf.
Dark-red Helleborine
E. atrorubens Schult.,
E. rubiginosa auct.

8–24 ins. Leaves oval-lanceolate to lanceolate, opposite-alternate, longer than their internodes. Flowers small, drooping, scented, and dark purple in colour. Ovary purple, pubescent. Label shorter than other divisions. Plant usually forming a clump, with several flowerheads. Widespread, in woods, and scrub up to over 4000 ft. 6–7. See page 22.

6 *Epipactis latifolia* (Huds.) All.
Broad Helleborine ·
E. helleborine Crantz

8–24 ins. Leaves large, oval, much longer than their internodes. Sepals greenish, petals tinted violet and label violet with brownish base, but colours very variable. Widespread in woods and scrub, up to 4500 ft. 7–8. See page 22.

Epipactis purpurata Sm.
Violet Helleborine

8–28 ins. Plant violet washed, generally forming clumps. Leaves oval, about as long as their internodes. Flowers numerous, in a compact spike, with outer divisions greenish, and inner ones whitish, washed green. Mainly in Beech woods, in northern Europe, rare in Switzerland. 8–9. See page 22.

Epipactis microphylla (Ehrh.) Sw.
Small-leaved Helleborine

8–24 ins. Plant washed purple. Leaves small, and always shorter than their internodes. Flowers small, with divisions greenish, edged purple, borne widely spaced, only a few per stem. Very local, in limestone woods, up to 3600 ft. 6–8. See page 22.

1

2

3

4

5

6

Plate 13

ORCHIDACEAE (*continued*)

The following Orchids are all found in, more or less, dense woodland

1 *Listera ovata* L.
Twayblade

8–20 ins. Leaves oval, 2 in number, and borne opposite, on the stem. Flowers greenish, in a long, loose spike. Label 2-lobed, vertical. Remaining divisions inturning to form a hood. Common. 5–7. See page 22.

2 *Listera cordata* L.
Lesser Twayblade

2–8 ins. Leaves, heart-shaped, opposite, set half-way up stem. Flowers greenish, tinted purplish-brown. Label with 2 pointed lobes and 2 small appendages at the base. Other divisions extended, star-like. Local. Mossy Mountain woods, from about 4000–7000 ft. 5–8. See page 22.

3 *Goodyera repens* L.
Creeping Lady's Tresses

4–10 ins. Plant stoloniferous, with stems arching ascendant. Leaves oval, reticulate. Flowers greenish-white, in an almost unilateral, slightly spiral, spike. Local in mossy woods, mainly Pine woods, up to over 5000 ft. 7–8. See page 22.

Spiranthes aestivalis (Poir.) Rich.
Summer Lady's Tresses

4–12 ins. Plant with 2–3 narrow leaves at the base. Flowers small, white veined green, arranged spirally round the stem. Uncommon, in marshy meadows, up to about 4000 ft. 7. See page 22.

Spiranthes autumnalis Rich.
Autumn Lady's Tresses

4–14 ins. Plant with leafless stem, and basal rosette of leaves. Flowers white inside, and greenish outside. Label white, with centre green. Flowers grouped in a dense, narrow, spiral. Damp meadows, up to 2700 ft. 8–9. See page 22.

4 *Neottia nidus-avis* L.
Bird's nest Orchid

8–16 ins. A yellowish-brown saprophytic Orchid. Stem scaly. Flowerhead robust, many flowered. Label with widely divergent terminal lobes. Widespread, in deep woods. 5–6. See page 22.

5 *Epipogium aphyllum* (F. W. Schmidt) Sw.
Leafless Epipogium, Ghost Orchid
E. gmelinii Rich.,
Epipogon aphyllum auct.

4–8 ins. A leafless saprophyte, with coral-like rootstock. Flowers large for the size of the plant, drooping, pale yellow, like the stem, but sometimes streaked violet. Label directed upwards while the other divisions hang, translucid, downwards. Spur violet, ascendant. Irregular in flowering, and may lie dormant for several years at a time. Found rarely in deep oldstanding Pine or Beech woods, up to nearly 6000 ft. 7–8. See page 22.

6 *Corallorhiza trifida* Chatel.
Coral-root
C. innata R.Br.

4–10 ins. A greenish-white saprophytic Orchid. Rootstock like coral. Flowers small greenish-white, with label white, spotted purple. Flower stems solitary or, more often, in groups. Local, mossy woods, from 4000 to nearly 6000 ft. 5–7. See page 22.

Plate 14

POLYGONACEAE

1 *Rumex scutatus* L.
French Sorrel

10–20 ins. Leaves about as broad as long, bluntly arrow-head shape, grey-green on limy soil. Male and female flowers on same plant. Widespread up to 7500 ft. 5–8.

Rumex nivalis Hegetschw.
Mountain Dock

3–8 ins. Ground leaves roundish-oval, cordate, or hastate. Stem with not more than 2 leaves. Male and female flowers on separate plants, red. Limestone screes, from 4500–7500 ft. 7–8.

2 *Oxyria digyna* L.
Mountain Sorrel

2–8 ins. Leaves kidney-shaped, slightly emarginate. Stem with up to 2 leaves, often with none. Fruit bordered by a wide red ring. Non-limy screes, from 5000–9000 ft. 7–8.

3 *Polygonum bistorta* L.
Snakeweed, Bistort

8–32 ins. Leaves flat, sharply retracting, at the base, to winged petioles. Flowers bright pink, borne in an erect, compact, spike. Widespread on damp, acid ground, from about 1500 to over 7000 ft. 5–7.

4 *Polygonum viviparum* L.
Alpine Bistort, Sprouting Knotgrass

4–10 ins. Leaves inrolling at their edges. Flowers rose to whitish, inter-mingled with bulbils, and borne on a narrow spike. The bulbils may often be seen to be sprouting, while still on the flowerhead. Widespread, in meadows, from 2000–9000 ft. 6–8.

5 *Lychnis viscaria* L.
Viscid Campion
Viscaria vulgaris Bernh.

12–24 ins. Leaves lanceolate, opposite, in pairs. Stem very sticky under the nodes. Flowers large, rosy-purple, borne on a stiff, candelabra-like spike. Petals entire. Very local, on banks, in meadows, and by edges of woods, from 900 to over 5000 ft. 5–7.

6 *Lychnis alpina* L.
Alpine Campion, Red Alpine Catchfly
Viscaria alpina L.

2–5 ins. Leaves lanceolate. Stem not viscid. Flowers small, clear purple, borne in a tight terminal head. Petals notched. Local, in poor alpine meadows, from about 6000 ft to over 9000 ft. 7–8.

1

2

3

4

5

6

Plate 15

CARYOPHYLLACEAE

Silene acaulis L.
**Cushion Pink,
Moss Campion**

Forms moss-like cushions on the rocks and screes. Prefers limestone. Flowers borne on very short stems, rose, occasionally white, notched at the tip. Widespread. From about 4000–9000 ft. 6–8.

1 ssp. *longiscapa* Kerner
Long-stemmed Moss Campion

More loosely growing, and has longer flower stems than the type.

2 ssp. *exscapa* All.
Stemless Moss Campion
S. exscapa All.

The lime-avoiding form of *S. acaulis*, forming even more smoothly mossy cushions, and with smaller flowers, scarcely rising above the leaves. Petals, often almost unnotched. Central and southern Alps. 6–8.

3 *Silene rupestris* L.
Rock Silene

4–8 ins. An Annual. Stem branching from the base, flowers small, white, arranged in a loose cyme. Lime avoiding. Widespread, from about 2000 to over 8000 ft. 7–8.

4 *Silene saxifraga* L.
Saxifrage-like Silene

4–8 ins. Plant glandular-viscid in its upper parts. Stems branching. Flowers small, greenish-white above, and greenish-red below, borne singly, at the tips of the branches. Prefers limestone. Local on rocks and screes, from about 2000 to over 7000 ft. 5–8.

5 *Silene vulgaris* Garcke
Bladder Campion
S. cucubalus Wibel

12–24 ins. Prefers limestone. In its alpine form, this familiar meadow plant may be found as high as 9000 ft. 6–9.

6 *Gypsophila repens* L.
Creeping Gypsophila

2–6 ins. An Annual. Leaves bluish-green, slightly fleshy. Flowers small, white, or pale rose. Petals only faintly notched. Widespread, on limestone, from 3600–8000 ft. 5–8.

1

2

3

4

5

6

Plate 16

CARYOPHYLLACEAE (*continued*)

1 *Lychnis flos-cuculi* L.
Ragged Robin

12–24 ins. This common British wild flower is widespread in the damp alpine meadows, up to over 7500 ft. 5–8.

2 *Lychnis flos-jovis* L.
Flower of Jupiter

12–24 ins. Leaves grey and woolly. Flowers over 1 in across, carmine, with pale reverse, arranged in a compact cyme. In Switzerland, in the Valais (Vispertal), Tessin, Fribourg and Grisons. Very local, on sunny slopes, up to about 6000 ft. 6–7.

3 *Silene nutans* L.
Nottingham Catchfly

12–24 ins. This uncommon British plant may be found as a common wayside flower of the limestone districts. Stem very viscid. Petals narrow, deeply incised, and dull white in colour. Up to 6900 ft. 5–7, or later.

4 *Silene dioica* L.
Red Campion
Lychnis dioica L., L. diurna Sibth., Melandrium dioicum (L.) Coss. & Germ., M. rubrum Garcke

This very common British wild flower may be found in the Alps, up to nearly 7000 ft. 4–9.

Silene elisabethae Janchen
Elisabeth's Campion
Melandrium elisabethae Rohrb.

4–8 ins. Stems arising from the axils of the leaves of a central rosette. Flowers very large, up to over $1\frac{1}{2}$ ins across. Petals violet-purple and deeply notched. This rare and beautiful plant is a native of the south-eastern Alps, between L. Como and L. Garda, from 3000–6000 ft. 7–8.

5 *Petrorhagia nanteuilii* Burnat
Proliferous pink
Tunica prolifera (L.) Scop., Kohlrauschia prolifera auct., Dianthus prolifer auct.

4–16 ins. Stems almost simple, with small, compact, terminal flowerheads. Flowers pink, 2–6 per head, and closely enveloped with brownish scales. Dry meadows and waysides, up to about 3000 ft. 5–9.

6 *Dianthus barbatus* L.
Sweet William

12–24 ins. The wild form of this well-known garden plant occurs, occasionally, in the sub-alpine regions. 6–8.

Plate 17

CARYOPHYLLACEAE (*continued*)

1   *Dianthus carthusianorum* L.
Chartreuse Pink

8–20 ins. Leaves linear, enfolding the stem, at the base. Flowers purple, in a tight terminal head. Bracts, enclosing the flowerhead, brownish, papery with sharply-pointed tips. Differing forms are to be found in the Valais and Tessin. Widespread, on dry, limestone slopes and rocks in the south and west Alps, up to 7500 ft. 6–10.

2   *Dianthus seguieri* Vill.
Seguier's Pink
D. chinensis L., var. asper

8–20 ins. Leaves linear, barely enfolding the stem. Bracts green, and not papery. Flowers purple above, and paler below, and with a circlet of darker spots around the gorge. Tessin, Grisons and southern Alps, from 2400 to nearly 5000 ft. 6–8.

3   *Dianthus superbus* L.
Fringed Pink

12–24 ins. Stem tall, branching, with several large, heavily-fringed flowers per stem. Flowers rosy-lilac, with greenish flecks at the base of the petals. Open woods, and meadows. Fairly common in the Grisons, local elsewhere. 6–9.

4   *Dianthus hyssopifolius* L.
Hyssop-leaved Pink

8–16 ins. Plant with several flowering stems. Flowers smaller than the above, less heavily fringed, and pale lilac to whitish in colour. Limestone meadows, mainly in the south and west, up to 6000 ft. 7–8.

Dianthus monspessulanus L.
Montpellier Pink

A local form of *D. hyssopifolius*. Southern Alps.

Dianthus sternbergii Sieb.
Sternberg's Pink

A local form of *D. hyssopifolius*. South-eastern Alps.

Dianthus caryophyllus
5   ssp. *sylvestris* Wulfen
Wood Pink

To 24 ins. A sub-species of *D. caryophyllus* which is not wild in the Alps. Stem often single flowered. Flowers large, rose, almost scentless. Limestone rocks, and dry slopes, up to 7500 ft. 6–8.

6   *Saponaria officinalis* L.
Bouncing Bet, Soapwort

16–30 ins. Stem erect. Flowers large, pale rose to white (occasionally double), borne in a loose spike. Common, by the waysides, from the plains, up to 4000 ft. 7–9.

1

2

3

4

5

6

Plate 18

CARYOPHYLLACEAE (*continued*)

1   *Dianthus gratianopolitanus* Vill. **Cheddar Pink** D. caesius Sm.

4–8 ins. Leaves grey-green. Flowers bright rose, slightly fringed, scented, and borne singly. The petals are bearded round the gorge. Local to rare. Limestone rocks, and stony meadows, up to over 6000 ft. 5–7.

2   *Dianthus neglectus* Loisel. **Indeterminate Pink**

2–6 ins. Superficially similar to the above, but with larger, more heavily fringed flowers, of a brighter rose colour. Petals with cream reverses, and not bearded at the gorge. Calyx purplish, and its supporting bracts are almost as long as the calyx tube, narrowly pointed, and divergent. Rare. Mainly confined to the southern and south-western Alps. Stony pastures, from 3600–9000 ft. 7–8.

3   *Dianthus glacialis* Hänke **Glacial Pink**

1–2 ins. Flower stems shorter than the leaves, which are grey-green, linear-lanceolate, obtuse. Flowers bright rose. An eastern Alpine, only found in Switzerland, east of a line Lenzerheide/Avers. Rare. High limestone meadows and rocks between 6000–8400 ft. 7–8.

4   *Dianthus alpinus* L. **Alpine Pink**

1–8 ins. Stem with 2–3 pairs of leaves. Flowers large, rose, dotted purple and white around the gorge. A rare gem from the Austrian Alps, on poor limestone meadows, and found between 3000 and 6000 ft. 6–8.

5   *Saponaria ocymoides* L. **Rosy Soapwort**

8–12 ins. A trailing rock plant, with branching stems. Flowers bright rosy-purple, occasionally white. Limestone rocks. Common in places, up to 6000 ft. 5–9.

6   *Saponaria pumilio* (St. Lag.) Janchen **Dwarf Soapwort** Silene pumilio Wulfen

Plant dwarf, cushion forming. Leaves downy. Flowers large, rosy, borne singly, on very short stems, only just above the leaves. Rare. Stony ground, in the East Dolomites, and Austrian Alps, from about 5000–8000 ft. 7–9.

    Saponaria lutea L. **Yellow Soapwort**

2–4 ins. Stem simple, hairy at the top. Flowers pale yellow, dotted blackish-violet at the gorge. Rare, on limestone rocks, in the southern Alps (Mt Cenis), from 4500 to nearly 8000 ft. 7–8.

Plate 19

CARYOPHYLLACEAE (*continued*)

1 *Cerastium arvense* L.
ssp. *strictum* Hänke.
**Field Mouse-ear
Chickweed**

A dwarf form of the common Chickweed, which occurs, in the Alps, up to 9000 ft. 4–7.

2 *Cerastium latifolium* L.
**Broad-leaved Mountain
Chickweed**

2–4 ins. Leaves oval, grey-green. Flowers large with wide petals, borne 2 or more per stem. Limestone moraines and screes, from 5400–9000 ft. 7–8.

3 *Cerastium uniflorum* Clairv.
One-flowered Chickweed

Rather similar to the above, but leaves grass-green, flowers smaller, with narrower petals borne only 1 per stem. Lime-free moraines and rocks, from 6000 to over 9000 ft. 7–8.

4 *Minuartia sedoides* L.
Mossy Cyphel
Cherleria sedoides L.,
Arenaria sedoides Kittel

1–2½ ins. A low-growing cushion plant, with yellowish-green flowers, which may be found, on limestone rocks and screes, between 5000 and over 9000 ft. 7–8.

5 *Minuartia verna* L.
Vernal Sandwort
Arenaria verna L.

2–4 ins. An herbaceous cushion plant. Leaves linear, tapering to a fine point. Sepals with 3 prominent nerves. Flowers small, white. Rocky limestone slopes, up to 9000 ft. 7–8.

6 *Minuartia recurva* All.
Recurved Sandwort

2–8 ins. Rootstock somewhat woody. Leaves linear, fleshy, all arching to one side. Sepals with 5–7 nerves. Petals white, slightly longer than the sepals. Lime-free screes, up to 9000 ft. 7–8.

1

2

3

4

5

6

Plate 20

CARYOPHYLLACEAE (*continued*)

1 *Minuartia villarsii* Balb.
Villar's Sandwort

4–8 ins. Stems ascendant, numerous. Leaves linear, flat, and weakly 3-nerved. Sepals with 3 nerves. Petals narrow, gradually attenuate at the base, faintly emarginate at the tips, and twice as long as the sepals. Rocky places in the southern Alps, doubtful in Switzerland. 7–8.

Minuartia laricifolia L.
Larch-leaved Sandwort

3–10 ins. Calyx truncate at the base. Pedicel and calyx pubescent, rather than glandular. Non-limy rocks and screes, up to 6000 ft. 7–8.

2 *Minuartia biflora* L.
Two-flowered Sandwort

Less than 4 ins. Leaves with not more than 1 nerve. Flowers white, borne, 1–2 per stem, on short downy pedicels. Sepals obtuse, hooded at the apex. Local. 7–8.

3 *Moehringia ciliata* Scop.
Ciliate Sandwort

2–6 ins. Prostrate. No upstanding branches, as in the case of *Minuartia*. Leaves linear, with 1–2 not very prominent nerves. Sepals sub-obtuse, slightly shorter than the petals. Flowers white. Limestone screes. From 3000 to over 8000 ft. 7–8.

Moehringia muscosa L.
Mossy Sandwort

3–12 ins. Leaves soft, and very narrow. Leaves and sepals with only 1 nerve. Flowers small, white, with only 4 petals. Damp limestone rocks, from 900–7000 ft. 6–8.

4 *Arenaria biflora* L.
Two-flowered Sandwort

3–12 ins. Stem trailing, rampant. Leaves sub-orbicular obtuse, tapering to a ciliated petiole at the base. Flowers solitary, or in pairs. Sepals with only 1 nerve. Rocky non-limy slopes. Local. 7–8.

5 *Arenaria ciliata* L.
Ciliate Sandwort

1½–5 ins. Plant with non-flowering rosettes. Leaves oval, ciliate at their base, and pointed. Stems with 1–2 flowers. Sepals with 1–3 nerves. Rough ground, from 3000 to over 9000 ft. 7–8.

6 *Arenaria grandiflora* L.
Greater Sandwort

2–5 ins. Leaves lanceolate, pointed at their tips, edges thickened, and with median nerve prominent below. Flowers large, white, with petals 2–2½ times as long as the sepals. Rare. Jura (Chasseron). 5–7.

Plate 21

RANUNCULACEAE

1 *Trollius europaeus* L.
Globe Flower

4–20 ins. Flowers globular, yellow, many-petalled. Widespread, in mountain meadows, up to 7500 ft. 5–7.

2 *Caltha palustris* L.
Marsh Marigold,
Kingcup

6–12 ins. This well-known spring flower is common in the Alps, and may be seen in full bloom, round the glacial meres of such passes as the Little St Bernard and Oberalp, as late as early August.

3 *Actaea spicata* L.
Baneberry,
Herb Christopher

12–32 ins. Leaves with 3 divisions, of 3 leaflets each. Flowers small, white in a tight, oval, head. Berries black. Local. Mountain woods, up to 4500 ft. 5–7.

4 *Paeonia officinalis* L.
Wild Paeony

24–36 ins. Flowers large, single, clear rose, sweetly scented. Local and mainly in the southern Alps. South Tessin (Mt Generoso), Italian Alps (Mt Baldo), etc. 900–4500 ft. 5–6.

5 *Helleborus foetidus* L.
Stinking Hellebore

8–16 ins. Stems many flowered, and very leafy at the base. Flowers bell-shaped, formed by purple bordered, greenish, petaloid sepals. Widespread, on dry, stony, limestone slopes, up to 4500 ft. 3–4.

6 *Helleborus viridis* L.
ssp. *occidentalis* (Reut.) Schiffn.
Green Hellebore

6–12 ins. Flowers large, green, widely open, and borne singly, or with only a few flowers per head. Very local, in woods, bushes, and in meadows mainly on limestone. Limone (Col de Tende). Up to 4500 ft. 3–4.

1

2

3

4

5

6

Plate 22

RANUNCULACEAE (*continued*)

1 *Aquilegia vulgaris* L.
Common Aquilegia, Columbine

12–36 ins. Stems with 3–12 flowers, up to 2 ins across, blue to dark violet, occasionally rose, or white. A variable plant. Widespread, in woods and bushy places, mainly on limestone. Up to 6000 ft. 5–7.

Aquilegia reuteri Boiss.
Reuter's Aquilegia

12–20 ins. Stem leaves divided into linear segments. Stamens not longer than petals. Flowers bright blue. Very local, and confined to the south-west French Alps. 6–7.

2 *Aquilegia alpina* L.
Alpine Aquilegia

8–28 ins. Stems with 1–3 flowers, 2–3 ins across. Flowers blue, and buds cream. Very local, in light woods, and bushy places, from 4500–6600 ft. 6–8.

3 *Aquilegia einseleana* F. W. Schultz
Einsel's Aquilegia

6–16 ins. Flowers small, rich violet, with short spurs, inturning till they almost meet, borne 1–3 per stem. Local, and confined to the southern Alps. Italy; and South Tessin only, in Switzerland. Absent in the French Alps. 7–8.

4 *Delphinium consolida* L.
Forking Larkspur

4–20 ins. Flowers brilliant blue, borne on numerous, few-flowered, branches. Locally abundant, on waste ground and mainly on limestone, up to over 4000 ft. 6–10.

Delphinium elatum L.
Wild Delphinium, Candle Larkspur

40–60 ins. The wild form of the garden Delphinium. Flowers dark blue, borne in a dense, erect spike. Rare in Switzerland except in the east. Dauphine, Pyrenees and eastern Alps. Banks of streams, and in meadows, among other tall-growing plants, from 3600–6000 ft. 7–8.

5 *Aconitum napellus* L.
Monk's Hood

20–60 ins. Flowers dark blue, with hood about as tall as wide, borne in a dense, simple or branching spike. Widespread on damp, rocky mountain pastures, up to 7500 ft. 6–7.

6 *Aconitum paniculatum* Lam.
Panicled Monk's Hood

30–60 ins. Flower stem much branching, and with no main terminal head. Flowers dark blue, with hood a little taller than wide. Less common than the above and found in clearings and bushy places, from 3000–7000 ft. 7–9.

Aconitum variegatum L.
Variegated Monk's Hood

32–60 ins. Differs from the above in that the hood is about twice as high as wide, and has a pronounced beak. Grisons, and Lower Engadine. Rare. 7–9.

Aconitum cammarum L.

A hybrid Monk's Hood. A garden plant, sometimes to be found naturalised. Flowers large, violet-blue, variegated with white. Hood ciliate at the edge. Stamens with woolly filaments. Flower spike large, dense and branching. Local. 7–9.

1

2

3

4

5

6

Plate 23

RANUNCULACEAE (*continued*)

1   *Aconitum anthora* L. **Poisonous Monk's Hood**

10–24 ins. Stem very leafy. Leaves palmate, very finely segmented. Flowers sulphur-yellow, with hood almost as broad as tall. Extremely local, in semi-shady places, mainly on limestone, in the Jura, Pyrenees, French and Italian Alps, between 1500–6600 ft. 7–9.

2   *Aconitum lycoctonum* auct. non L. **Yellow Monk's Hood** A. vulparia Rchb.

20–60 ins. Leaves palmate, with segments shield-shaped to lanceolate. Flowers yellow, in a loose, simple or branching spike. Hood at least three times as high as wide. A variable species, the form shown is *vulparia*. Widespread, in mountain woods, up to nearly 7000 ft. 6–8.

   Aconitum ranunculifolium Rchb. **Buttercup-leaved Monk's Hood**

20–24 ins. Similar to the above, but smaller, with spike usually simple, leaves with narrow segments, divided almost to the base, and flowers with hoods only about twice as high as wide. Less common, except in the south and east. 7–8.

3   *Clematis alpina* L. **Alpine Clematis** Atragene alpina L.

Climbing or trailing. Flowers large, blue, 4-petalled. Light woods, stony and bushy places, and mainly in the southern and eastern Alps. In Switzerland only in the Grisons. From 3000–7000 ft. 5–7.

4   *Hepatica nobilis* Schreb. **Hepatica** H. triloba Chaix., Anemone hepatica L.

2–6 ins. Ground leaves markedly 3-lobed. Stem leaves verticillate, closely below the flower, and simulating a calyx. Flowers blue, pink or white. Abundant in places. Woods, from 1200 to over 6000 ft. 3–5 or even 6.

5   *Anemone trifolia* L. **Three-leaved Anemone**

4–12 ins. Leaves with, as a rule, 3 lanceolate, finely and evenly toothed segments. Flowers yellowish-white. Anthers white. Local, in woods, in the southern Alps, up to 5000 ft. 5–6.

   Anemone nemorosa L. **Wood Anemone**

Similar to the above but much more common. Leaves with 3–5 irregularly toothed segments. Flowers smaller, more drooping, white, veined or tinted violet-pink on the outside. Very common, in woods, up to over 5000 ft. 3–5.

6   *Anemone narcissiflora* L. **Narcissus-flowered Anemone**

8–24 ins. Flowers pink in bud and white when fully open, borne 3–8 per stem, in a terminal head. Locally plentiful, on limestone, between 4500–7000 ft, but at lower altitudes on the Jura, where it may be seen to its best advantage on the Chasseron. 5–7.

Plate 24

RANUNCULACEAE (*continued*)

1   *Anemone ranunculoides* L.
Yellow Wood Anemone,
Wood Ginger

6–10 ins. Ground leaves 0–1. Stem leaves verticillate, divided to their base. Segments pointed. Flowers small, 5–8-petalled, golden-yellow, borne singly, or 2–3 per stem. Local. Mainly on limestone, in the southern Alps, up to 4500 ft. 3–5.

2   *Anemone baldensis* Turra
Mt Baldo Anemone

2–5 ins. Flowers white, with undersides of petals pink tinged, and hairy. Petals 8–10 in number. Seedheads not plumose (distinguishing feature between *Anemone* and *Pulsatilla*). Local, in the southern Alps, from about 5000 to over 8000 ft. 6–8.

3   *Pulsatilla alpina* L.
Alpine Pasque Flower
Anemone alpina L.
4   ssp. *sulphurea* L.
Yellow Alpine Pasque
Flower

4–12 ins. Flowers large, white, tinged, more or less, violet, on the reverse Seedheads plumose. Widespread, on limestone meadows, from 3000–8000 ft. 6–8.
A sub-species of *P. alpina*, and exactly similar, except for the yellow colouring of the flowers and its preference for non-limy soil. Widespread. 6–8.

5   *Pulsatilla vernalis* L.
Spring Pasque Flower
Anemone vernalis L.

2–6 ins. Flowers 6-petalled, white, with silky-haired, violet reverse. Stem and leaves also covered with long silky hairs. Flowers as the snow recedes, and is found on non-limy soil, up to over 9000 ft. 3–6.

6   *Pulsatilla halleri* All.
Haller's Pasque Flower
Anemone halleri All.

4–12 ins. Leaves very silky-haired. Mature flowers large, widely open, erect, and clear violet in colour. A rare plant, found, in Switzerland, only in the Valley of St Nicolas. French and Italian Alps. 3000–9000 ft. 5–7.

Pulsatilla montana Hoppe
Mountain Pasque Flower
A. montana Hoppe

4–12 ins. Flowers dark violet, not erect, but drooping. Local, in the Valais and Grisons, up to 6000 ft. 4–5.

Pulsatilla vulgaris Mill.
Pasque Flower
A. pulsatilla L.

Flowers violet-lilac, or reddish-brown (*P. rubra*). Jura, Ain, north-east Grisons, up to 2400 ft. 3–4.

Plate 25

RANUNCULACEAE (*continued*)

1   *Ranunculus aconitifolius* L.
White Bachelor's Buttons, Fair Maids of Kent

8–40 ins. Stem branching, many-flowered. Leaves palmate, divided down to the petiole. Branches spreading, and flowers borne on short pedicels, white. Common on damp ground, up to 7500 ft. 5–7.

2   *Ranunculus alpestris* L.
White Alpine Buttercup

2–6 ins. Leaves small, palmate, bright green, and shiny. Flowers white, with rather irregularly shaped petals. Widespread. Limestone rocks, from 5000–8400 ft, but at much lower altitudes in the Jura. 4–9.

3, 4   *Ranunculus glacialis* L.
Glacial Buttercup

2–8 ins. Leaves palmate, greyish-green, fleshy. Flowers large, white, turning to pink, rose and finally, old rose. Petals persistent, withering without dropping. Common on damp rocks, and screes sparsely covered with vegetation, from 7000–12,000 ft. 7–8.

5   *Ranunculus seguieri* Vill.
Seguier's Buttercup

2–6 ins. Plant hairy, but glabrous later. Leaves palmate, with 3–5 narrowly acuminate segments. Flowers white, borne, 1–3 per stem. Petals drop before fading, and do not turn pink, as in the above. In Switzerland, only in the Alps de Brienz. In the French Jura at Le Reculet. Also in the Dauphine, southern and eastern Alps, and Dolomites (Sella Pass). Rare, on damp limestone screes, and humus, from 5400–7000 ft and over. 6–7.

6   *Ranunculus parnassifolius* L.
Grass of Parnassus-leaved Buttercup

2–6 ins. Leaves entire, broadly lanceolate to cordate, hairy at the edges, but glabrous later. Flowers pink in bud opening to white, tinged pink. In Switzerland, only in the northern limestone Alps, and in the Grisons. A western Alpine, which is strictly local and found between 3700–8700 ft. 6–8.

Plate 26

RANUNCULACEAE (*continued*)

1 *Ranunculus platanifolius* L.
Plane-leaved Buttercup

To 48 ins. Considered, by some, to be a sub-species of *R. aconitifolius*, Plate 25, and differing in having the leaves not divided to the petiole, its larger flowers, borne on longer, erect, pedicels, and its preference for dry ground. Though less common it is, nevertheless, widespread, in clearings and scrubland, from 1500–4500 ft. 6–8.

2 *Ranunculus pyrenaeus* L.
Pyrenean Buttercup

2–6 ins. Leaves lanceolate, entire. Stems bear 1–5 white flowers. Petals drop very early, and litter the ground, like confetti. Locally plentiful in the central and southern Alps, on damp, non-limy soil, between 5000 and to over 8000 ft. 5–7.

3 *Callianthemum coriandrifolium* Rchb.
Coriander-leaved Callianthemum
Ranunculus rutaefolius L.

Leaves glabrous, bi-pinnate, with segments much overlapping. Flowers white, tinged pink outside, with 5–10 sepals and petals. Petals obovate, wider than long. A rare gem of the very high snow valleys, in the southern and western Alps, between 5400–9000 ft. 7–8.

4 *Callianthemum kerneranum* Freyn
Kerner's Callianthemum

$1\frac{1}{2}$–$2\frac{1}{2}$ ins. Similar to the above, but smaller and with at least 10 linear-oblong, pink backed petals. This rare little gem is a native of the southern Alps, where it may be found in the topmost screes of the mountains round L. Garda. 5–7.

5 *Ranunculus thora* L.
Poisonous Buttercup

4–10 ins. Ground leaves usually lacking. Stem with 1 large, sub-orbicular-reniform leaf crenulated at the tip, and 1–2 linear to tri-lobed leaves, higher up. Flowers yellow, 1–5 per stem. Local. Limestone meadows in the west and south, from 3000–6000 ft. 5–7.

6 *Ranunculus × hybridus* Biria
Hybrid Buttercup

2–4 ins. Like a miniature *R. thora*, but with ground leaves persistent, and stem leaves with deeply incised lobes. Native of the south-eastern Alps. Absent elsewhere. Found from 3000 to over 6000 ft. 6–8.

Plate 27

RANUNCULACEAE (*continued*)

1 *Ranunculus montanus* Willd.
Mountain Buttercup
R. geraniifolius Pourr.

2–16 ins. Base leaves Geranium-like with 3–5 segments, toothed at the tip. Upper leaves with linear-lanceolate segments. Flowers golden-yellow, borne 1–3 per stem. Widespread, from 2000 to over 8000 ft. 5–8.

2 *Adonis vernalis* L.
Spring Adonis

4–12 ins. No ground leaves. Leaves much divided and embracing the stem. Flowers large, pale yellow and with 10–20 petals. Dry limestone meadows, and in heathland. Local. 4–5.

3 *Adonis flammeus* Jacq.
Pheasant Eye

8–10 ins. Leaves very finely divided. Flower scarlet-red, sometimes black in the centre. Seed with a beak-like tooth. Meadows, up to 4500 ft. 5–7.

4 *Thalictrum aquilegifolium* L.
Columbine-leaved Meadow Rue

16–45 ins. Leaves like *Aquilegia*. Flowers pale violet, or white, in showy feathery plumes. Local. Damp meadows and thickets, up to 6000 ft. 5–7. There are several other species of *Thalictrum* to be found in the Alps, all with rather inconspicuous heads of flowers, and often difficult to identify.

PAPAVERACEAE

5 *Papaver pyrenaicum* Kerner
ssp. *rhaeticum* Leresche
Orange Alpine Poppy
P. aurantiacum Loisel.

6 ins. Leaves small, pinnate. Sepals covered with brown hairs. Flowers yellow, turning to orange. May be seen in huge drifts, on the terminal moraine of the Cambrena glacier, Bernina Pass. Southern and eastern Alps, between 6000–8000 ft. 7–8.

Papaver suaveolens Lapeyr. and *P. sendtneri* Kerner

A small yellow form, *P. suaveolens*, is to be found in the Pyrenees, and a white form, *P. sendtneri*, in the northern limestone Alps, Château d'Oeux, Mt Pilatus.

6 *Papaver alpinum* L.
Alpine Poppy

6 ins. Similar to the above, but leaves even more finely divided, and flowers white, tinged yellow at the base of the petals. Confined to the western and northern limestone Alps, Savoy, Jura, Bernese Oberland, Pennine Alps. 7–8. This small yellow form occurs in the Austrian Alps.

ssp. *kerneri*
Kerner's Alpine Poppy

Plate 28

BERBERIDACEAE

1 *Berberis vulgaris* L.
Barberry

3–6 ft. A spiny shrub. Leaves oboval. Flowers yellow, in pendant clusters. Widespread on limestone, but often absent elsewhere. Found up to 6000 ft. 5–6.

FUMARIACEAE

2 *Corydalis lutea* L.
Yellow Fumitory or
Corydalis

4–10 ins. Leaves greyish-green, much divided. Flowers bright yellow. Southern Alps. 5–9.

CRUCIFERAE

Owing to the very large number of species belonging to this Family, it is only possible to give it token coverage. For this reason, only the more interesting species, and those most typical of the High Alps, have been included.

3 *Thlaspi rotundifolium* L.
Round-leaved Penny Cress

2–6 ins. Leaves roundish. Flowers pale lilac, or white, in compact hemispherical heads. Fragrant. Local. Limestone screes, from about 5000 to over 9000 ft. 6–9.

4 *Thlaspi corymbosum* J. Gay
Corymbose Penny Cress

A dwarf form of the above, found on non-limy soil. Base leaves narrower. Pedicels of the individual flowers arising from almost the same point on the stem, the flowerhead appears almost flat on top, in the form of a corymb. Rare. In the Valais (Gornergrat), Tessin and Grisons. 6–9.

5 *Thlaspi perfoliatum* L.
Perfoliate Penny Cress

4–10 ins. Leaves cordate at their base, embracing the stem. Flowers white, in a loose head. Common, up to 5000 ft. 4–6.

6 *Thlaspi montanum* L.
Mountain Penny Cress

4–8 ins. Non-flowering shoots long, stoloniferous. Ground leaves oboval, attenuate in petiole. Stem leaves winged at base. Flowers white. Anthers yellow or white. Flowerhead hemispherical at first, lengthening later. Seedpod oval, widely winged. Style longer than 2 mm. Local. Rocky limestone meadows, from 900–6000 ft. 4–5.

Thlaspi alpestre L.
Alpine Penny Cress

12–16 ins. Leaves inclined to be blue-green. Shoots not lengthening to stolons. Flowerhead lengthening greatly, with age. Anthers yellow, violet or blackish. Petals small, shield-shaped, white. Seedpods narrow, widely winged. Style not exceeding 2 mm. Non-limy meadows, from 3000–6000 ft. 5–6.

Plate 29

CRUCIFERAE (*continued*)

1 *Cardamine pentaphyllos* L.
Five-leaved Bitter Cress
Dentaria digitata Lam.

12–20 ins. Leaves palmate, with 3–5 leaflets. Flowers showy, violet. Lime-stone woods. Locally abundant, from 1200–6600 ft. 5–7.

2 *Cardamine heptaphylla* Vill.
Seven-leaved Bitter Cress
Dentaria heptaphylla Lam.

12–24 ins. Leaves pinnate, with 5–7 (usually 7) leaflets. Flowers equally showy, white, or pale lilac. Common in places. Limestone woods, up to about 5000 ft. 4–5.
C. pentaphyllos and *C. heptaphylla* may often be seen together.

Cardamine bulbifera L.
Coralroot
Dentaria bulbifera L.

12–24 ins. Lower leaves pinnate, with 5–7 segments. Upper leaves undivided. Violet bulbils borne in the axils of the leaves. Flowers pale lilac, with narrow petals. Local, in Beech woods, up to about 4800 ft. 4–5.

Cardamine polyphylla O. E. Schultz
Many-leaved Bitter Cress
Dentaria polyphylla Waldst.
& Kit.

10–16 ins. Leaves pinnate, with 7–9 leaflets. Flowers yellowish-white. Very local, in mountain woods, mainly in the southern Alps, up to about 4800 ft. 4–5.

3 *Biscutella laevigata* L.
Yellow Biscutella

4–24 ins. Lower leaves entire, or toothed. Upper leaves linear to lanceolate. Flowers yellow to pale yellow. Seedpods shield-shaped, in pairs. Widespread, in rocky places, from 1500–7800 ft. 5–8.

4 *Cheiranthus cheiri* L.
Wallflower

12–18 ins. Stem woody at base. Leaves narrow, nearly white below. Flowers golden-yellow, scented. Local, up to about 1800 ft. 5–6.

5 *Lunaria annua* L.
Honesty
L. biennis Moench.

15–30 ins. Leaves oval-acuminate, sessile above, and petiolate below. Flowers large, purplish to violet, scented by night. Seedpods silvery-white, disc-like. Waysides. 5–6.

Lunaria rediviva L.
Perennial Honesty

15–30 ins. Rather similar to the above, but with all leaves petiolate, flowers lilac to violet veined, and seedpod longer and narrower. Perennial. Strongly scented. Prefers limestone. To the north of woods, up to over 4000 ft. 5–7.

Matthiola tristis (L.) R.Br.
6 ssp. *valesiaca* J. Gay
Alpine Stock

4–12 ins. Stem very leafy at base. Flowers pale violet, scented. Rare. Mainly found in the Valais on the north side of the Simplon Pass. 5–7.

1

2

3

4

5

6

Plate 30

CRUCIFERAE (*continued*)

1 *Petrocallis pyrenaica* L.
Rock Beauty, Pyrenean Rock Cress
Draba pyrenaica L.

1–4 ins. A cushion plant, with stems rampant, mostly underground. Leaves trifid, in rosettes. Flowers rose, lilac or white. Local, on limestone screes, between 5000–9000 ft. 6–7.

2 *Hutchinsia alpina* L.
Common Alpine Cress

1½–6 ins. Ground leaves pinnate. Stem usually leafless. Flowers white. Plant forms compact clumps. Limestone rocks, and screes, from about 3300 to over 10,000 ft. 6–7.

3 *Draba aizoides* L.
Yellow Whitlow Grass

2–4 ins. Leaves stiff, linear, in tight rosettes. Flowers bright yellow. Widespread. Limestone rocks, from 4200–9600 ft. 2–8, according to altitude and aspect.

Erysimum sylvestris Crantz
4 ssp. *helveticum* Jacq.
Swiss Blister Cress

2–20 ins. Leaves linear-lanceolate. Flowers bright yellow and scented. Rough ground, in the Valais, Tessin and Grisons. 6–8.

5 *Cardamine resedifolia* L.
Mignonette-leaved Bitter Cress

1–5 ins. Leaves pinnate, with 3–7 leaflets. Petioles with winged bases. Flowers white, 6–12 per head, the outer ones opening first. Widespread, on damp rocks, gravels, and in snow valleys, from 2000 to well over 10,000 ft. 7–8.

Cardamine alpina (L.) Willd.
Alpine Bitter Cress
C. bellidifolia L.

1–3 ins. Leaves lozenge-shaped, simple and slightly fleshy. Petioles not winged at base. Flowers white, 2–6 per head and flowering at the same time. Damp gravels, and non-limy meadows, from 4500–10,000 ft. 7–8.

Isatis tinctoria L.
Woad

12–48 ins. Stem and leaves grey-green. Stem leaves arrow-shaped, embracing the stem. Flowers yellow, borne in ample heads. Seedpods drooping, green turning to purple. The plant from which the ancient Britons are said to have obtained the blue dye, for colouring their bodies, in preparation for battle. Frequently to be seen in the upper Rhône Valley (Valais) and elsewhere, on waste ground. 4–6.

6 *Kernera saxatilis* L.
Rock Kernera

4–12 ins. Ground leaves entire, dentate, or slightly pinnate, grouped in a basal rosette. Stem leaves sessile. Flowers white. Widespread, on limestone rocks, between 1200–3800 ft. 5–7.

1

2

3

4

5

6

Plate 31

CRUCIFERAE (*continued*)

1   *Arabis alpina* L.
Alpine Rock Cress

3–10 ins. Stem leafy. Leaves grey-green, toothed and embracing the stem. Flowers white. Widespread on limestone, from 2400–9000 ft. 5–9.

2   *Arabis bellidifolia* Jacq.
Daisy-leaved Rock Cress
A. jacquinii Beck

4–10 ins. Lower leaves hairless, almost entire, in basal rosettes. Stem leaves 5–12, hairless at the edges, and semi-embracing. Flowers white. Widespread, from 5400–8400 ft. 6–7.

3   *Arabis pumila* Jacq.
Dwarf Rock Cress

2–4 ins. Ground leaves covered with stellate hairs. Stem with 1–4, sessile, non-embracing leaves. Flowers white, 4–6 per stem. Damp limestone rocks, from 2000 to over 8000 ft. 6–7.

   Arabis coerulea All.
Blue Rock Cress

1–4 ins. Ground leaves blue-green, tridentate, usually hairless. Stem leaves 1–3, ciliate at the edge. Flowers bluish, few in number. Uncommon. Limestone rocks, and snow valleys. From about 6000 to over 10,000 ft. 7–8.

4   *Iberis saxatilis* L.
Rock Candytuft

2–5 ins. Plant sub-shrubby at the base. Leaves linear, entire, slightly fleshy. Flowers white, occasionally rose. Limestone rocks and gravels, from 1200–7500 ft. 5–7.

5   *Draba tomentosa* Clairv.
Hairy Whitlow Grass

1–2½ ins. Leaves covered with a tomentum of starry hairs. Stem also starry-haired, leafless or with up to four leaflets. Flowers white. Seedpods oval, hairy at the edges, and, as a rule, on the sides. Local. Limestone rocks, from 6000 to over 10,000 ft. 7–8.

   Draba dubia Suter
Indeterminate Whitlow Grass

1–4 ins. Rather similar to the above, but stem with only a few starry hairs, and with seedpod longer, narrower, as a rule, and hairless. Rocks, from about 4000 to well over 9000 ft. 5–7.

6   *Lepidium draba* L.
Hoary Cress or **Pepperwort**
Cardaria draba (L.) Desv.

12–28 ins. Leaves sinuate-dentate, winged at the base, and embracing the stem. Flowers small, white and very numerous, borne in a dense corymb. Waste places, often in masses, and found up to about 6000 ft. 4–7.

1

2

3

4

5

6

Plate 32

CRASSULACEAE

1 *Sempervivum arachnoideum* L.
Cobweb Houseleek

2–5 ins. Plant with rosettes of succulent leaves, covered with white, web-like tomentum (very variable in quantity). Flowers with 8–12, bright rose, petals, each with darker central stripe. Widespread, on lime-free rocks, from 1200–9000 ft. 7–9.

2 *Sempervivum montanum* (L.) Jacq.
Mountain Houseleek

4–6 ins. Rather similar to the above, but rosettes not covered with tomentum and flowers violet-rose, with 12–16 petals, which are narrowly pointed, and have a darker central stripe. Widespread, on lime-free soil, from 4500–9000 ft. 7–8.

Sempervivum tectorum L.
3 ssp. *alpinum* Griseb & Schenk.
**St Patrick's Cabbage,
Common Houseleek**

6–14 ins. The true species occurs in the Jura, but the sub-species, *alpinum*, is more likely to be found in the Alps. This differs, in having smaller rosettes, of more longly acuminate leaves, which are less regularly, and less stiffly ciliate at their edges. Flowers with 12–16, dull rose petals. Rocks, up to over 8000 ft. 7–8.

Sempervivum wulfenii Hoppe
Yellow Houseleek

4–10 ins. Leaves of rosettes ciliate at their edges and red at the base. Flowers whitish-yellow with 12–16 petals. Uncommon. Lime-free rocks. 7–9.

4 *Sedum telephium* L.
Livelong, Orpine

8–20 ins. Stem erect. Leaves succulent, toothed at their edges. Flowers yellow, borne in a tight corymb. Plant variable. Rocky places, up to over 5000 ft. 7–9.

5 *Sedum album* L.
White Stonecrop

4–12 ins. Plant with non-flowering rosettes. Leaves succulent, linear-cylindrical. Flowers white, or pale rose. Walls, and rocky places, up to 7500 ft. 6–8.

6 *Sedum rupestre* L.
Rock Stonecrop

6–12 ins. A variable species. Branches of flowerhead drooping before the flowers open. Leaves linear, pointed. Flowers usually bright yellow. Found up to about 6000 ft. 6–7.

1   2   3

4   5   6

Plate 33

CRASSULACEAE (*continued*)

1   *Sedum alpestre* Vill.
Alpine Stonecrop

1–2 ins. Leaves green, succulent, half-round in section. Flowers yellow. Petals pointed, and sepals blunt. Lime-free rocks, from about 3000 to over 10,000 ft. 6–8.

2   *Sedum acre* L.
Wall Pepper, Stonecrop

3–5 ins. Leaves pale green. Flowers yellow. Common up to over 6000 ft. 6–7.

3   *Sedum atratum* L.
Dark Stonecrop

1–3½ ins. Leaves reddish, small, succulent, and half-round in section. Flowers whitish, greenish or reddish, borne in tight heads. Limestone rocks, from 3000–8200 ft. 7–8.

SAXIFRAGACEAE

SECTION I. LEAVES OPPOSITE, IN PAIRS

4   *Saxifraga oppositifolia* L.
Opposite-leaved Purple Saxifrage

Plant trailing. Flowers purple, solitary, on short, erect stems. Anthers greyish-violet. Damp limestone rocks, from about 5400 to well over 10,000 ft. 6–8.

5   *Saxifraga biflora* All.
Two-flowered Saxifrage

More loosely trailing than the above, and with 2–9 flowers per stem. Petals narrow, violet, occasionally lilac or white. Anthers orange-yellow. Damp limestone rocks, from 6600–9600 ft. 7–8.

Saxifraga retusa Gouan
Dull-red Saxifrage

A similar Saxifrage, from the southern Alps. Flowers 2–3 per stem. Petals purple. Anthers yellow. Very rare in Switzerland. Shady rocks 6000–9000 ft. 5–6.

SECTION II. MARKED BASAL ROSETTES OF LEAVES

Saxifraga mutata L.
Orange-red Saxifrage

4–20 ins. Stem glandular-sticky in its upper half. Flowers with very narrow, reddish-orange petals, borne in dense spikes. Damp limestone rocks, in the southern and eastern Alps, from 2000 to about 4500 ft. 6–8.

6   *Saxifraga cotyledon* L.
Greater Evergreen Saxifrage

12–24 ins. Leaves strap-shape, in large basal rosettes. Flower stem branching from the base, and often drooping at the tip. Flowers white. Local. Damp non-limy rocks and gorges. 5–8.

Plate 34

SAXIFRAGACEAE (*continued*)

SECTION II (*continued*). MARKED BASAL ROSETTES OF LEAVES

1 *Saxifraga aizoon* Jacq.
Evergreen Saxifrage

2–12 ins. Leaves stiff, wedge-shaped, succulent, white-toothed at the edge in compact basal rosettes. Stem branching in its upper half. Flowers whit usually dotted red. Widespread on rocks, from 3600–9000 ft. 5–8.

2 *Saxifraga hostii* Tausch
Host's Saxifrage

Rather similar to the above, but with long, narrow, leaves, curving down their tips, and of very local distribution in the Italian Alps. Prefers limeston 6–7.

3 *Saxifraga rotundifolia* L.
Round-leaved Saxifrage

8–16 ins. Base leaves sub-orbicular-reniform, toothed at the edges, an borne on long petioles. Stems leafless, bearing many white flowers, wit petals spotted red, and tinged yellow at the base. Local. Damp rocks an shady places, from 1500–7500 ft. 6–9.

4 *Saxifraga cuneifolia* L.
Shield-leaved Saxifrage

4–8 ins. Leaves obovate, tapering to a long petiole and toothed at their edge Flowers pendant, white, spotted yellow and red, and borne in a loose spik Widespread, in woods, and shady places, from 4500–6000 ft. 6–8.

5 *Saxifraga stellaris* L.
Starry Saxifrage

3–6 ins. Leaves nearly sessile, obovate, clearly toothed at their edges. Stem leafless. Flowers white, star-like, with narrow petals, usually spotted orang Widespread. Damp rocks, and by streams, from 3600–9000 ft. 6–8.

6 *Saxifraga androsacea* L.
Androsace-like Saxifrage

2–4 ins. Leaves spatulate, entire, or toothed at the edge. Stems few flowered Flowers white, with petals twice as long as the sepals. Lime-containing soi from 5400 to well over 8000 ft. 5–8.

1

2

3

4

5

6

Plate 35

SAXIFRAGACEAE (*continued*)

1   *Saxifraga caesia* L. $1\frac{1}{2}$–4 ins. Plant forming hemispherical, or almost spherical, mounds of tigh
Blue-green Saxifrage   grey-green rosettes from which rise few-flowered stems, bearing large pur
white flowers. Local, on limestone rocks and debris, from 5400–8000 ft. 7–8

2   *Saxifraga aizoides* L.   2–8 ins. Leaves small, fleshy, pale green, lanceolate, and ciliate at the edges
Yellow Mountain Saxifrage,   Flowers yellow to flaming orange-red. Widespread on damp screes, and
Evergreen Saxifrage   gravels, and beside streams, from 2400–9000 ft. 7–8.

3   *Saxifraga aspera* L.   2–6 ins. Plant forming loose clumps. Leaves sharply pointed at their tips
Rough Saxifrage   and spinily ciliate at their edge. Stems with 5–7 flowers. Petals white with
orange spots. Non-limy rocks and screes, up to about 6000 ft. At the highe
elevations, its place is taken by the sub-species *bryoides*. 7–8.

4   ssp. *bryoides* L. $1\frac{1}{2}$–$2\frac{1}{2}$ ins. Rosettes small, bright green, forming smoothly mossy clumps
Mossy Saxifrage   Flowers large, white spotted orange, often borne singly. Widespread. Lime
S. bryoides L.   free rocks and screes, from about 5400–9600 ft. 7–8.

5   *Saxifraga seguieri* Spreng.   1–3 ins. Plant loosely moss-like. Leaves lanceolate to spatulate, glandular
Seguier's Saxifrage   ciliate at their edges. Petals pale yellow, about as long and wide as the sepals
The dead leaves are without white tips, in which it differs from *S. muscoides*
Plate 36. Damp, non-limy rocks, in the central and southern Alps, betwee
6600–9000 ft. 7–8.

6   *Saxifraga exarata* Vill.   1–4 ins. Plant mossy. Leaves with 3–5 lobes. Dead leaves deeply furrowe
Furrowed Saxifrage   below. Petals yellowish-white to white, about twice as wide as the sepals an
considerably longer. Lime-free rocks, and screes, from 6000 to over 9000 ft
7–8.

   Saxifraga moschata Wulfen   1–4 ins. Leaves generally not more than 3-toothed and sometimes even entire
Musky Saxifrage   Flowers greenish-yellow, with petals about as broad and a little longer tha
S. varians Sieb.   the sepals. A very variable species. Limestone rocks and screes, from 4800–
9000 ft. 7–8.

1

2

3

4

5

6

Plate 36

SAXIFRAGACEAE (*continued*)

1   *Saxifraga muscoides* All.
Smooth-leaved Saxifrage
S. planifolia Lap.

1–2 ins. Leaves linear-lanceolate, ciliate at the edges, and forming tight mats on the ground. Stems with 2–5 flowers. Petals whitish-yellow, occasionally lemon-yellow, and about twice as long, and wide, as the sepals. Local. Damp, non-limy rocks, between 6900–9000 ft. 7–8.

2   *Chrysosplenium alternifolium* L.
Alternate-leaved Golden Saxifrage

2–8 ins. Leaves alternate, kidney-shaped. Flowers yellow. Damp, shady places, up to the alpine regions. 3–6.

  Chrysosplenium oppositifolium L.
Opposite-leaved Golden Saxifrage

Similar to the above, but forming denser clumps, and with leaves opposite and not alternate. In similar situations, but more widely distributed than the above. 3–7.

PARNASSIACEAE

3   *Parnassia palustris* L.
Grass of Parnassus

2–12 ins. Ground leaves cordate. Stem leaves, one, semi-embracing. Flower large, white and borne singly. Autumn flowering. Damp mountain meadows up to 7500 ft. Widespread. 7–9.

ROSACEAE

4   *Aruncus sylvestris* Kostel.
Goat's Beard, Wood Spiraea
Spiraea aruncus L.

3–6 ft. Leaves large, bi-pinnate, with oval-acuminate segments, double saw-toothed at the edge. Flowers small, whitish, in a very showy plume. Found up to 4500 ft and prefers a non-limy soil. 6–7.

5   *Amelanchier ovalis* Medic.
Snowy Mespilus
A. rotundifolia Dum.-Cours.,
A. vulgaris Moench.

3–6 ft. Shrub. Leaves ovate, dentate, cottony below. Flowers white with very long, narrow petals. Fruit blue-black. Rocky places mainly on limestone, up to about 5400 ft. 4–5.

6   *Fragaria vesca* L.
Wild or **Woodland Strawberry**

2–10 ins. Plant self-fertile, with long stolons. Stamens barely as long as the styles. Sepals inclined to be reflexed at maturity. Woods. Common, up to nearly 6000 ft. 5–6.

1

2

3

4

5

6

Plate 37

ROSACEAE (*continued*)

1 *Potentilla rupestris* L.
Rock Cinquefoil

8–24 ins. Stem erect, usually tinted red. Lower leaves pinnate and upper leaves trifoliate. Flowers white. Local, in rocky and bushy places, mainly on non-limy soil, up to about 6600 ft. 5–7.

2 *Potentilla caulescens* L.
Stalked Cinquefoil

4–12 ins. Leaves green, trifoliate. Flowers ragged, white, in a many-headed inflorescence. Locally abundant, on limestone rocks, from about 2000–6600 ft. 7–8.

3 *Potentilla nitida* L.
Glossy Cinquefoil

1–4 ins. Leaves trifoliate, silvery, silky-haired. Flower stem short, with 1 large single flower per stem. Flowers white, in the Grande Chartreuse, and bright rose in the Dolomites, and Bergamasque Alps. Local, on dolomitic limestone, up to 9000 ft. 7–9.

4 *Potentilla aurea* L.
Spotted Cinquefoil

2–12 ins. Leaves palmate, with 5–7, obovate, dentate, leaflets, the terminal tooth being much smaller than the others, and the whole edged with silvery hairs. Flowers golden-yellow, with, usually, an orange spot at the base of each petal. Widespread, on lime-free soil. 3300–8400 ft. 6–8.

5 *Potentilla crantzii* Crantz
Alpine Cinquefoil

4–12 ins. Plant pubescent. Leaves not edged with silvery hair, and terminal tooth about equal to the others. Flowers golden-yellow, but without the orange spot at the base of the petals. Otherwise very similar to *P. aurea* but found on limy soil, from 3000–9000 ft. 7–8.

6 *Rubus saxatilis* L.
Rock Blackberry, Stone Bramble

4–10 ins. Stems with a few weak spines. Leaves with 2 sessile side leaflets, and 1 longly petiolate, terminal leaflet. Flowers small, white. Berry scarlet. Mountain woods, up to nearly 7000 ft. 5–6.

Plate 38

ROSACEAE (*continued*)

1 *Alchemilla pentaphylla* L.
Five-leaved Lady's Mantle

1–3 ins. Trailing. Leaves almost hairless, with 5 leaflets, the middle 3 bein oboval shield-shape, very deeply incised at their tips. Local. Damp meadow: and snow valleys, from 6300–8900 ft. 7–8.

2 *Alchemilla conjuncta* Bab.
Joined-leaved Lady's Mantle
A. hoppeana Rchb.

4–12 ins. Leaves with 7–9 segments, all more or less joined at their bases Flowers borne well above the leaves. Widespread, on limy soil, from 3600 7800 ft. 5–8.

Alchemilla alpina L.
Alpine Lady's Mantle

4–12 ins. Leaves with 5–7 segments, all more or less divided at their bases Flower stems no taller than the leaves. Lime-free soil, from 3600–7800 ft 6–8.

3 *Geum reptans* L.
Creeping Mountain Avens
Sieversia reptans L.

2–6 ins. Leaves pinnate, with side and end leaflets about the same size Leaf stems, and flower stems often tinged red, as are the long strawberry like runners, which may extend up to 4 ft from the parent plant. Spectacula flowers, of clear golden-yellow, and up to over 2 ins in diameter. The flowe featured on the 10 Fr. Swiss Bank note. Damp, scantily clad, rocky places from 6400–9000 ft. 7–8.

4 *Geum montanum* L.
Mountain Avens
Sieversia montana L.

4–12 ins. Leaves pinnate, with irregularly divided side segments, and mucl larger terminal segment. Flowers golden-yellow, up to over 1 in in diameter Widespread, from 4800–8400 ft. 5–8.

5 *Geum rivale* L.
Water Avens

12–24 ins. Flowers drooping. Sepals brownish-red. Petals pale yellow, witl darker veining, and often tinted reddish-brown. Widespread, by streams and in mountain meadows, from 1200–6000 ft. 5–7.

6 *Dryas octopetala* L.
Mountain Avens, White Dryas

A much branching sub-shrub, with longish oval leaves, crenulate at thei edges, shiny dark green above, and white tomentose below. Flowers large pure white, borne on long pedicels. Limestone rocks. Common, in places from 3600–7500 ft. 5–8.

1

2

3

4

5

6

Plate 39

ROSACEAE (*continued*)

1   *Rosa pendulina* L.
    Alpine Rose
    R. alpina L.

20–80 ins. Flower stem generally spineless. Flowers bright rosy-carmine. Widespread, from 1500–7800 ft. 5–8.

LEGUMINOSAE

2   *Genista pilosa* L.
    Hairy Greenweed

4–16 ins. Stems ascendant. Flowers yellow, borne in terminal spikes. Dry, rocky places. Locally abundant, up to over 4000 ft. 4–10.

3   *Genista tinctoria* L.
    Dyer's Greenweed

A sub-shrub, growing up to 36 ins. Stems erect, bearing long spikes of yellow flowers. Wings and keel, turning down, and at a wide angle from the standard. Widespread, in clearings and by the wayside, up to over 5000 ft. 4–8.

4   *Genista sagittalis* L.
    Feathered Broom
    Cytisus sagittalis Koch

6–10 ins. Stems ascendant, winged and leafy. Leaves simple, sessile. Flowers yellow, borne in a terminal spike. Widespread, in meadows, and by the waysides, up to about 2700 ft. 5–7.

5   *Cytisus nigricans* L.
    Black Broom

12–40 ins. Leaves trifoliate, with obovate leaflets. Flowers yellow, borne in a narrow leafless spike. A native of the southern Alps. 6–7.

6   *Cytisus sessilifolius* L.
    Sessile-leaved Broom

3–6 ft. Leaves all with 3 leaflets. Leaves sessile. Flowers yellow, borne in a terminal head, above the leaves. Limestone areas of the southern Alps, up to about 3600 ft. 4–7.

Plate 40

LEGUMINOSAE (continued)

1 *Cytisus radiatus* (L.) Mert. & Koch
Rayed Broom
Genista radiata Scop.,
Cystanthus radiatus (L.) Lang

12–32 ins. Stem much branched with branches opposite, or verticillate. Leaves opposite, with linear, trifoliate, leaflets. Flowers yellow, borne in terminal clusters. Dry, rocky places in the Vaud, Valais, Lower Engadine and in the southern and south-eastern Alps, on limy soil, from about 2400–6000 ft. 5–8.

2 *Cytisus hirsutus* L.
Hairy Broom

12–32 ins. Stem, young leaves, branches, and seedpods covered with downy hairs. Flowers entirely yellow, or with standard flecked brown, borne 1–3, in the axils of the leaves of last year's branches, and never with a terminal head of flowers. Fairly plentiful, in the southern Alps, up to about 5700 ft. 4–6.

Cytisus emeriflorus Rchb.
Coronilla-leaved Broom

12–24 ins. Leaves oblong, obtuse and apiculate. Flowers yellow, borne laterally, 1–3, in the axils of the leaves. Southern Alps. 6.

3 *Colutea arborescens* L.
Bladder Senna

3–12 ft. Leaves pinnate, with 3–6 pairs of side leaflets. Flowers large, golden yellow, with standard streaked brown, borne 2–8, on long pedicels, arising from the axils of the leaves. Seedpods very large, tinged purple, and much inflated, mature during the following year. Local in the southern Alps, up to 4500 ft. 5–7.

4 *Ononis rotundifolia* L.
Round-leaved Restharrow

6–16 ins. Leaves sub-orbicular, dentate, and glandular-pubescent. Flowers rose, borne in few-flowered heads, on common pedicels, arising from the axils of the leaves. Open, sunny, woods, up to over 5000 ft. 5–7.

5 *Ononis natrix* L.
Goat Root, Yellow Restharrow

8–20 ins. Plant glandular-hairy. Leaves oblong-elliptic, dentate. Flowers large, axillary, golden-yellow, with standard veined brown. Prefers limestone. Arid slopes up to about 4800 ft. 6–8.

6 *Ononis spinosa* L.
Prickly Restharrow L.
O. campestris Koch & Ziz

12–24 ins. Stem erect, or ascendant, always with spiny branches. Flowers rose, purple, occasionally violet or white, borne axillary, singly, or in pairs. Widespread, up to over 5000 ft. 6–9.

Ononis repens L.
Restharrow
O. arvensis auct.

Similar to the above, but very rarely spiny. Stem downy all round. Leaves oval and hairy, instead of oblong and glabrescent, and seedpod shorter than the calyx. Equally common. 6–9.

Plate 41

LEGUMINOSAE (*continued*)

1 *Astragalus sempervirens* Lam.
   Evergreen Milk Vetch
   A. aristatus L'Herit

2–8 ins. Petioles with spines at their tips. Plant covered with whitish hair. Leaves pinnate with 6–10 pairs of leaflets. Flowers axillary, white, washed violet, shorter than the leaves. Local, on rocky limestone slopes, up to over 7000 ft. 5–6.

2 *Astragalus monspessulanus* L.
   Montpellier Milk Vetch

4–8 ins. Plant stemless. Flower stems and leaves rising from the base of the plant. Leaves with 10–20 pairs of side leaflets. Flowers bright purple, with wings not divided, and standard much longer than the wings. Seedpods ascendant, and incurving. Prefers limestone. Dry slopes, and gravels, mainly in the southern Alps, up to 6600 ft. 5–7.

3 *Astragalus onobrychis* L.
   Sainfoin Milk Vetch

4–10 ins. Stem not longer than 12 ins. Leaves with 8–12 pairs of side leaflets. Flowers sessile, purplish-blue, with standard three times as long as the wings. Flowerhead lengthening with age. Dry slopes and gravels, on limestone, up to 5700 ft. 5–8.

4 *Astragalus glycyphyllos* L.
   Milk Vetch, Wild Liquorice

12–48 ins. Long stemmed, and trailing. Leaves with 4–6 pairs of side leaflets. Flowers pale greenish-yellow, borne in tight heads, on pedicels arising from the axils of the leaves. Widespread, on dry slopes, and in bushy places, mainly on limestone, up to about 4500 ft. 6–8.

5 *Astragalus leontinus* Wulfen
   Lepontine Milk Vetch

6–8 ins. Stems short. Leaves with 6–9 pairs of side leaflets. Flowers sessile, purplish-blue, with standard quite twice as long as the wings which are rounded at their tips. Calyx with black hairs. Local, on dry limy slopes, from 3000–7800 ft. 6–7.

6 *Astragalus alpinus* L.
   Alpine Milk Vetch

4–8 ins. Stem short. Leaves with 8–12 pairs of side leaflets. Standard washed blue, and no longer than the keel, which is white, tipped violet. Wings whitish, narrower and shorter than the keel. Prefers a non-limy soil, and is found from about 5700–7800 ft. 7–8.

1

2

3

4

5

6

Plate 42

LEGUMINOSAE (*continued*)

1 *Astragalus australis* L.
Southern Milk Vetch

2–12 ins. Leaves with 4–7 pairs of narrow side leaflets. Flowers on pedicels, drooping, yellowish-white, with standard longer than keel. Wings deeply cleft at their tips, and longer than the keel. Keel violet tipped. Local. Rock-strewn meadows and screes, on non-limy soil, from 5700–9000 ft. 7–8.

2 *Astragalus exscapus* L.
Stemless Milk Vetch

2 ins. Plant stemless. Flowerheads shorter than leaves. Leaves with 12–15 pairs of side leaflets, elliptic to lanceolate, and covered with long, silky hairs, as in the whole plant. Flowers bright yellow, practically stemless and forming a golden cushion on the ground. Rare. Dry, bushy, limestone slopes, from 1500–6600 ft. 5–7.

Astragalus depressus L.
Short-stemmed Milk Vetch

2–4 ins. Leaves with 9–11 pairs of sub-orbicular leaflets which are hairy below. Flowers yellowish-white, often washed blue, borne on stems shorter than the leaves. Seedpod nearly cylindrical. Local. Southerly-facing, rocky, lime-stone slopes, from 2400–8000 ft. 5–7.

3 *Phaca alpina* L.
Pendulous-flowered Milk Vetch
Astragalus pendiflorus Lam.

8–24 ins. Stems branching pubescent and erect. Leaves with 9–11 pairs of side leaflets. Flowers yellow, drooping, borne in compact heads on pedicels, arising in the axils of the leaves. Seedpods pendant, much inflated, and reminiscent of *Colutea arborescens*, Plate 40. Rocky, bushy, limestone slopes from 4200–7200 ft. 7–8.

4 *Phaca frigida* L.
Glacial Milk Vetch
Astragalus frigidus A. Gray

6–16 ins. Stem not branching and not downy. Leaves with 4–5 pairs of side leaflets. Flowers drooping, yellowish-white, in a compact head and borne on pedicels arising from the axils of the leaves The presence of a terminal leaflet effectively distinguishes this plant from *Lathyrus levigatus*, the Yellow Everlasting Pea, Plate 47, in which the terminal leaflet is replaced by a short point.

Oxytropis: differs from *Astragalus* in that the keels of the flowers are terminated by a point. In *Astragalus* the tip of the keel is rounded.

5 *Oxytropis pilosa* (L.) DC.
Downy Beaked Milk Vetch
Astragalus pilosus

6–12 ins. Plant with well developed stem. Leaves with 9–13 pairs of downy leaflets. Plant covered with silvery down. Flowers yellow, borne in a compact head, on pedicels arising from the axils of the leaves. Gravels and waste places, mainly in the warmer valleys, on limestone, from 3000 to nearly 8000 ft. 5–8.

6 *Oxytropis campestris* (L.) DC.
Field Beaked Milk Vetch

2–6 ins. Plant hairy. Leaves with 10–15 pairs of side leaflets. Flowers erect palest yellow to white. Keel occasionally tipped dark violet. Rocky meadow and gravels, from 3000–9000 ft. 6–8.

Oxytropis foetida (Vill.) DC.
Stinking Beaked Milk Vetch

2–4 ins. Plant glandular-sticky. Leaves with 14–25 pairs of side leaflets. Flowers yellowish. Local. Rocky, non-limy slopes, from 5400–9000 ft. 7–8.

1

2

3

4

5

6

Plate 43

LEGUMINOSAE (*continued*)

1   *Oxytropis montana* (L.) DC. **Mountain Beaked Milk Vetch**

2–6 ins. Plant nearly stemless, glabrous, or slightly downy. Leaves with 8–17 pairs of side leaflets. Flowers violet-blue to reddish, almost horizontal. Stipules small, and independent. Rocky limestone meadows, from 4500 to over 8000 ft. 7–8.

2   *Oxytropis lapponica* Wahlenb. **Lapland Beaked Milk Vetch**

2–6 ins. Plant nearly stemless, downy. Leaves with 8–14 pairs of leaflets. Calyx shortly tubular. Flowers violet, fading to livid blue and pendant. Stipules joined opposite the petiole. Local. Prefers a non-limy soil, and is found from about 5400 to over 8000 ft. 7–8.

3   *Oxytropis sericea* Simonk. **Hairy** or **Haller's Beaked Milk Vetch** O. halleri Bunge

2–8 ins. Plant stemless, silky haired. Leaves with 9–16 pairs of side leaflets. Flowers erect, violet, borne in an oval head, which lengthens with age. Prefers non-limy soil, and is found between 4500 and nearly 8000 ft. 4–7.

4   *Onobrychis viciifolia* Scop. **Sainfoin, Holy Clover** O. sativa Lam.

12–28 ins. Stem erect, or ascendant. Leaves with 6–12 pairs of side leaflets. Flowers pale purple, with standard darker veined, and as long as the keel. Very common, on limestone, up to 7500 ft. 5–9.

5   var. *montana* Lam. & DC. **Mountain Sainfoin** O. montana DC.

Stems trailing-ascendant. Leaves with 5–8 pairs of side leaflets. Flowers rosy-purple, with standard shorter than the keel, and often paler in colour. Tends to replace the above at the higher elevations. 7.

6   *Trifolium alpinum* L. **Alpine Clover**

2–8 ins. Leaves trifoliate, with narrow leaflets. Flowers large, purple, erect, borne in few-flowered heads. Common on lime-free soil. 6–8.

1

2

3

4

5

6

Plate 44

LEGUMINOSAE (*continued*)

1 *Trifolium pratense* L.
ssp. *nivale* Sieb.
Snow Clover

4–8 ins. The alpine form of *T. arvense*. Calyx hairy. Flowers white, turning to rose later. Common, up to over 7000 ft. 5–9.

2 *Trifolium thalii* Vill.
Thal's Clover

2–6 ins. Plant glabrous. Leaves oboval. Flowers white, turning to bright rose. Limestone meadows, from about 5200–8400 ft. 7–8.

3 *Trifolium badium* Schreb.
Brown Clover

4–8 ins. Small, tightly oval heads of yellow flowers, which turn brown on fading. Widespread. Limestone meadows, up to over 8000 ft. 6–8.

4 *Anthyllis vulneraria* L.
ssp. *alpestris* Hegetschw.
Alpine Kidney Vetch
A. alpestris Hegetschw.

A sub-species of *A. vulneraria*, with paler yellow flowers. Common. Limestone meadows, up to 9000 ft. 5–8.

5 *Anthyllis montana* L.
Mountain Kidney Vetch

4–6 ins. Plant with woody rootstock, stems and leaves silver haired. Leaves pinnate, with 10–13 pairs of side leaflets. Flowers bright rose, or purple, borne in tight heads at the tips of the stems. Local. Limestone rocks, from 1500–7000 ft. 6–7.

6 *Lotus corniculatus* L.
Bird's-foot Trefoil

4–12 ins. Trailing. Flowers in umbels of 3–8 flowers. Flowers yellow, often washed orange-red. Common. 5–7.

Lotus pedunculatus Cav.
Large Bird's-foot Trefoil
L. uliginosus Schkuhr.

12–20 ins. Similar to the above, but taller, more robust, with 8–15 flowers per head. Flowers plain yellow. Marshy ground. Common. 6–7.

Plate 45

LEGUMINOSAE (*continued*)

1 *Hedysarum obscurum* L.
Alpine Sainfoin
H. hedysaroides (L.) Sch.
& Thell.

4–10 ins. Stem erect, or ascendant. Leaves with 5–9 pairs of side leaflets. Flowers drooping, rich purple-violet. Local. Rocky meadows, from 4800–7500 ft. 7–8.

2a *Melilotus albus* Desr.
White Melilot

12–60 ins. This tall-growing plant is common on waste ground and by the wayside, up to about 4500 ft. 6–9.

2b *Melilotus altissimus* Thuill.
Yellow Melilot

12–40 ins. Often to be seen in quantity by the waysides, in company with the White Melilot, and up to about the same altitude. 6–10.

Melilotus officinalis Lam.
Common Melilot

12–40 ins. Differs from *M. altissimus*, in having the upper leaves lanceolate to elliptic instead of oblong-linear ; wings longer than the keel instead of being the same length and in the seedpod being glabrous instead of hairy. Equally common. 6–10.

3 *Vicia sylvatica* L.
Wood Vetch

20–48 ins. Trailing. Leaves with 6–12 pairs of leaflets. Flowers whitish, with standard veined violet. Local. Mountain woods, from 3000–6600 ft. 6–8.

4 *Coronilla coronata* L.
Yellow Crown Vetch
C. montana Jacq.

12–20 ins. Leaves with 4–6 pairs of leaflets. Flowers golden-yellow, in compact heads. Locally abundant. Rocky slopes, mainly on limestone, up to about 4500 ft. 5–7.

5 *Coronilla varia* L.
Crown Vetch

12–48 ins. Trailing. Leaves with 7–12 pairs of leaflets. Flowers with standard rose, wings white and keel white, tipped dark violet. Limestone areas, sometimes in great quantity, up to about 5000 ft. 5–8.

Coronilla emerus L.
Scorpion Senna

A shrub. 32–80 ins. Leaves with 2–4 pairs of side leaflets. Flowers yellow, axillary, usually in threes. Seedpod cylindrical. Locally abundant. Edges of woods and rocky places on limy soil, up to about 4000 ft. 4–7.

6 *Tetragonolobus maritimus* L.
Marsh Trefoil
T. siliquosus Roth.

4–12 ins. Leaves oboval, cuneate. Flowers sulphur yellow, borne singly. Common, in damp meadows, and ditches, up to nearly 5000 ft. 5–7.

Plate 46

LEGUMINOSAE (*continued*)

SECTION I. LEAVES WITH ONE PAIR OF LEAFLETS, AND TERMINAL TENDRILS

1 *Lathyrus tuberosus* L.
**Tuberous Vetchling,
Earth-nut Pea**

12–36 ins. Stem angular, unwinged. Flowers bright carmine, up to 5 per head. Clay, and chalk, up to about 5000 ft. 6–7.

Lathyrus pratensis L.
Yellow Meadow Vetchling

12–36 ins. Stem angular, unwinged. Flowers bright yellow, 4 or more per head. Common, up to about 6000 ft. 6–9.

Lathyrus sylvestris Retz.
Wild Pea

3–6 ft. Petioles with wings narrower than the stem. Flowers with standard rose, wings purplish and keel greenish. Woods. Widespread, up to over 5000 ft. 6–8.

2 ssp. *heterophyllus* L.

3–9 ft. Petioles with wings as wide as the stem. Lower leaves with only 1 pair of leaflets, but upper ones with 3 or 4 pairs. Flowers rose. Local, on dry slopes and in mountain woods, up to nearly 6000 ft. 7–8.

3 *Lathyrus latifolius* L.
Everlasting Pea

3–9 ft. Petioles widely winged. Leaflets broad. Flowers large, bright rose. Not common. At lower altitudes. 6–8.

SECTION II. LEAVES WITH 2–3 PAIRS OF LEAFLETS, AND WITHOUT TERMINAL TENDRILS

4 *Lathyrus montanus* Bernh.,
Bitter Vetch
L. macrorrhizus Wimm.,
Orobus tuberosus (L.) Tourn.

6–8 ins. Erect, stem winged. Leaves grey-green below. Flowers clear purple, later bluish. Mountain woods. Common, up to about 4000 ft. 4–5.

Lathyrus vernus (L.) Bernh.
5 var. *albus*
Spring Vetchling
Orobus vernus (L.) Tourn.

8–14 ins. Stem unwinged. Leaves broadly oval and longly acuminate. Flowers purple, later blue, and finally, livid ; occasionally white. Mountain woods. Common, up to nearly 6000 ft. 4–5.

SECTION III. LEAVES WITH 4–5, OR MORE, LEAFLETS, AND WITHOUT TERMINAL TENDRILS

6 *Lathyrus niger* L.
Black Bitter Vetch
Orobus niger (L.) Tourn.

12–36 ins. Stem not winged. Leaves with 4–6 pairs of narrow elliptic leaflets. Flowers bluish-purple, widely spaced, on a tall, narrow, head. Locally plentiful mainly on limy soil, up to over 4000 ft. 5–7.

1

2

3

4

5

6

Plate 47

LEGUMINOSAE *(continued)*

1 *Lathyrus levigatus* Waldst. & Kit.
Yellow Everlasting Pea
L. luteus (L.) Peterm.

12–36 ins. Stem erect, not winged. Leaves with 4–5 pairs of leaflets. Flowers large, numerous, in a compact head, pale yellow, ageing to orange-brown. Very local, on rocky limestone slopes, up to about 7000 ft. 6–7.

GERANIACEAE

2, 3 *Geranium sylvaticum* L.
Wood Cranesbill

12–24 ins. Leaves widely segmented. Flowers purple-violet, occasionally white. Widespread, up to 7500 ft. 6–8.

Geranium argenteum L.
Silver Cranesbill

3–5 ins. Plant silvery-white. Leaves with 5–7 lobes, divided almost to the petiole, each with 3 narrow lobules. Flowers pale rose. Uncommon. Western Alps (Dauphine), from 5000–6000 ft. 7–8.

4 ssp. *cinereum* Cav.
Ashy Cranesbill

4–6 ins. Leaves ash-green, divided into 5–7, trilobed segments. Petals pale rose, with darker veining. West and central Pyrenees, between 6000–7000 ft. 6–8.

Geranium phaeum L.,
5 var. *lividum* L'Herit
Livid Cranesbill

16–24 ins. Plant tall and unmistakable with its blackish-purple flowers, and much dilated, or even reflexed petals. Local, in the eastern Alps. Var. *lividum* with dull mauve flowers, is the form most likely to be seen in the western and southern Alps, up to over 7000 ft. 5–7.

6 *Geranium sanguineum* L.
Bloody Cranesbill

12–24 ins. Stem with long hairs. Leaves with 7 deeply incised segments. Flowers rosy-purple, borne solitary on long pedicels. Widespread on dry slopes and in clearings, up to 4500 ft. 6–9.

Plate 48

GERANIACEAE (*continued*)

1   *Geranium nodosum* L.
Knotted Cranesbill

8–16 ins. Leaves with 3–5 broadly oval, acuminate, segments. Flowers pinkish-violet, with darker veining. Local, mainly in the west and south, up to nearly 5000 ft. 6–8.

2   *Geranium palustre* L.
Marsh Cranesbill

12–32 ins. Leaves with 3–5 deeply-notched segments. Pedicels sharply reflexed after flowering. Flowers pale pinkish-purple, with darker veining. Widespread, in damp and shady places, up to 4500 ft. 6–9.

3   *Geranium rivulare* Vill.
White Cranesbill
G. aconitifolium L'Herit

8–24 ins. Leaves with 5–7 segments. Flowers white, veined purple. Local, in open woods, and bushy places, from 4500 to over 7000 ft. 6–8.

LINACEAE

4   *Linum alpinum* Jacq.
Alpine Flax

4–12 ins. Flowers large, clear blue. Limestone meadows, up to over 6000 ft. 6–7.

5   *Linum tenuifolium* L.
Narrow-leaved Flax

6–16 ins. Leaves narrowly linear, ciliate at their edges. Flowers pale rosy-lilac, fading almost to white. Dry limestone meadows, up to 4500 ft. 6–9.

6   *Linum viscosum* L.
Viscid Flax

12–24 ins. Plant glandular-sticky. Leaves oval to lanceolate. Flowers large, bright rose, with darker veining. Arid places in the southern Alps, up to over 5000 ft. 5–7.

1

2

3

4

5

6

Plate 49

EUPHORBIACEAE

1 *Euphorbia cyparissias* L.
Cypress Spurge

6–16 ins. Leaves narrow, numerous, on much branching stem. Flowers yellow, turning to brilliant orange-red. Out of all the many members of the Spurge Family this is, undoubtedly, the most beautiful, and the most typical of the Alpine scene. Widespread. 4–7.

POLYGALACEAE

2 *Polygala chamaebuxus* L.
Bastard Box, Yellow Shrubby Milkwort

2–12 ins. A sub-shrub, with evergreen leaves. Flowers axillary, yellow and white, with purple-brown tips. Limestone rocks, and rocky meadows. Widespread. 4–7.

3 var. *grandiflora* Gaudin
Red Shrubby Milkwort
P. chamaebuxus
var. purpurea Neilr.

A form of the above, with larger flowers, rose, tipped yellow, which is to be found in the Engadine, Tessin and southern Alps, where the two may sometimes be seen, in flower, together.

4 *Polygala alpestris* Rchb.
Mountain Milkwort

3–6 ins. Plant herbaceous. Leaves alternate. Flowers blue. Mountain meadows. 6–7.

5 *Polygala alpina* DC.
Alpine Milkwort

2–4 ins. Flower stems arising from the axils of the leaves, which have a flavour of herbs. Stems with 5–10 bluish flowers. Mainly in the southern Alps 6–8.

6 *Polygala vulgaris* L.
Common Milkwort

6–12 ins. A very variable species. Leaves alternate. Flowers blue, violet or rose, rarely white. Wings of flowers with reticulate veining. Widespread. 5–7.

1

2

3

4

5

6

Plate 50

CISTACEAE

1   *Helianthemum nummularium* L.
Common Rockrose
H. chamaecistus Mill.

4–16 ins. Plant inclined to be shrubby. Flowers large, golden-yellow. Widespread. 5–10.

2   *Helianthemum alpestre* Jacq.
Alpine Rockrose

4–6 ins. Leaves linear, oblong or oval, green on both sides. Flowers yellow, smaller than the above. Rocky meadows. Widespread. 6–7.

Helianthemum canum L.
Hoary Rockrose

4–8 ins. Similar to the above, but with leaves grey tomentose below. More local than the above, but may be found in the Jura, Ain and Savoy. 6.

3   *Helianthemum apenninum* L.
White Rockrose
H. polifolium Mill.

4–12 ins. A white flowered Rockrose, to be found in the Jura, Ain and Savoy. 5–6.

4   *Cistus albidus* L.
Tomentose Sunrose

3 ft. A shrub with white tomentose leaves. Flowers large, silvery-rose. Southern Alps, up to about 3600 ft. 5–6.

Cistus salvifolius L.
Sage-leaved Sunrose

12–24 ins. Leaves oval, tomentose below. Flowers large, white, yellowing with age. Southern Alps. 5.

VIOLACEAE

5   *Viola wolfiana* W. Becker
Wolf's Violet

2–4 ins. Leaves clear green. Flowers scented, pale violet, white at the throat, and with lower petals veined dark violet. Shady places. 4.

Viola pinnata L.
Pinnate Violet

2–4 ins. Leaves palmate, much divided. Flowers pale violet-blue. Limestone screes. Local. 6.

Viola palustris L.
Bog Violet

3–6 ins. Leaves reniform. Flowers lilac, with lower petals veined violet. Marshy ground, up to over 7000 ft. 4–6.

6   *Viola biflora* L.
Two-flowered Pansy

2–6 ins. Stems with 1–2 flowers, which are bright yellow, veined brown. Widespread, in damp and shady places, up to over 8000 ft. 6–8.

1

2

3

4

5

6

Plate 51

VIOLACEAE (*continued*)

1   *Viola calcarata* L.
Alpine Pansy

2–6 ins. Leaves oval to lanceolate, dentate. Flowers of variable shape and colours, from dark to pale violet, yellow or white. Widespread. 6–8.

2   *Viola lutea* Huds.
Mountain Pansy

4–8 ins. Stem usually simple. Stipules almost digitate. Flowers yellow or violet. Western Alps. 6–7.

3   *Viola dubyana* Burnat
Duby's Pansy

4–8 ins. A *Viola* common in the Italian Alps, between L. Como and L. Garda. 5–8.

Viola cenisia L.
Mt Cenis Pansy

1–4 ins. Leaves roundish, not dentate. Flowers violet. Stipules almost entire. Limestone screes, mainly in the west. 7.

4   *Viola tricolor* L.
Wild Pansy, Heartsease

4–10 ins. A very variable pecies, swith flowers of varying sizes and colours. 3–9.

RHAMNACEAE

5   *Rhamnus pumila* Turra
Dwarf Buckthorn

A sub-shrub, with tortuous branches, closely applied to the rock surfaces. Flowers greenish-yellow, 4-petalled. Rocks. 6.

GROSSULARIACEAE

6   *Ribes alpinum* L.
Alpine or **Mountain Currant**

24–60 ins. A shrub. Plant spineless. Flowers yellowish, erect rather than drooping. Bushy places. Widespread. 4–6.

1

2

3

4

5

6

Plate 52

ONAGRACEAE

1 *Epilobium angustifolium* L.
Rose-Bay Willowherb
Chamaenerion angustifolium
(L.) Scop.

18–50 ins. Flowers purple, occasionally white. Widespread. This well-known plant may be found in the Alps, up to about 7500 ft. 7–9.

2 *Epilobium dodonaei* Vill.
Rosemary-leaved Willow-herb
E. rosmarinifolium Hänke,
Chamaenerion dodonaei
(Vill.) Schur

12–36 ins. Stem erect, very leafy. Leaves very narrow, entire, as a rule. Lobes of the calyx rose, to pale rose, as are the petals. Locally plentiful. 6–9.

3 *Epilobium fleischeri* Hochst.
Fleischer's Willowherb

Not so tall growing as the above, and with stems ascendant, rather than erect. Leaves linear-lanceolate, toothed at their edges. Lobes of the calyx reddish brown. Petals rose to whitish-rose. Locally abundant, on screes, moraines, river gravels and waste ground, up to about 7500 ft. 7–8.

THYMELACEAE

4 *Daphne mezereum* L.
Mezereon

12–48 ins. A shrub. Begins to flower before the leaves appear. Flowers purple, scented, arising from the axils of the previous year's fallen leaves. Widespread, in woods and rocky meadows, mainly on limestone, up to about 6000 ft. According to altitude, 3–7.

5 *Daphne cneorum* L.
Garland Flower

4–12 ins. An evergreen sub-shrub. Young branches, and corolla tube pubescent. Flowers rosy-red, borne in terminal heads. Scented. Jura and western Alps. Local to rare. Prefers limestone. Up to about 6000 ft. 5–7.

6 *Daphne striata* Tratt.
Striated Daphne

4–12 ins. Very similar to the above, but with stems glabrous, duller rose flowers, very sweetly scented, and leaves mainly in verticels, below the terminal flowerhead. Its western limit in Switzerland is at Binn, in the Valais. Limestone meadows and Dolomite, mainly in the eastern Alps, up to over 8000 ft. 6–7.

Daphne alpina L.
Alpine Daphne
D. candida Vitm.

8–20 ins. Leaves soft, silky haired and deciduous. Flowers white, or greenish purple, and scented. Local on limestone, up to about 6000 ft. 4–5.

Daphne petraea Leybold
Rock Daphne
D. rupestris Facch.

A dwarf sub-shrub, with tortuous branches. Flowers rose, strongly scented. Limestone rocks and cliffs of the Alps between L. Garda and L. Idro. 6–7.

1

2

3

4

5

6

Plate 53

UMBELLIFERAE

1 *Astrantia major* L.
   Greater Masterwort

12–36 ins. Leaves palmate, with segments joined at the base. Flowers small, white or rosy in a compact, simple, umbel nestling in an involucre of leaves of a similar colour. Limestone meadows, up to about 6000 ft. 6–9.

2 *Astrantia minor* L.
   Lesser Masterwort

6–16 ins. Leaves palmate, with very narrow segments, divided to the base. Flowers white, in a small, simple, umbel. Prefers a non-limy soil, and is found in shady places, up to about 8000 ft. 7–8.

3 *Eryngium alpinum* L.
   Blue Thistle

12–30 ins. Plant glaucous. Ground leaves triangular-oval, and dentate. Flowers small, blue, massed on a central column which is surrounded by a large, saucer-like involucre of spiny, deeply dissected, blue leaves. This beautiful plant has its centre of distribution at Pralognan, in the French Alps, but may be found in favoured situations in Switzerland, up to about 7500 ft. 7–9.

4 *Meum athamanthicum* Jacq.
   Spignel, Bald Money

12–24 ins. Stem hollow. Plant strongly aromatic. Leaves feathery, doubly tri-pinnate. Flowers white, in a composite umbel. Non-limy soil, up to about 4500 ft. 6–8.

5 *Bupleurum stellatum* L.
   Starry Hare's Ear

4–16 ins. Leaves linear-lanceolate, erect, and with reticulate veining. Stem with not more than 1 leaf. Flowers yellowish, in a simple umbel, enfolded in an involucre of leaves, which are joined to about their middles. Non-limy rocks and meadows, from about 3000 ft to over 8000 ft. 7–8.

6 *Bupleurum longifolium* L.
   Long-leaved Hare's Ear

12–32 ins. Ground leaves oboval to oblong, tapering to a long petiole. Stem leaves oval, cordate at the base. Flowers reddish-yellow, surrounded by an involucre of leaves not joined at their edges. Rocky limestone meadows, mainly in the west, up to about 6000 ft. 7–8.

Plate 54

UMBELLIFERAE (*continued*)

1 *Bupleurum petraeum* L.
Rock Hare's Ear
B. graminifolium Vahl.

8–12 ins. Leaves grass-like, at the base of the plant. Stem leafless. Involucre star-like, not enfolding the few-flowered umbel. Local, on limestone rocks of the southern Alps, up to 6000 ft. 7–8.

2 *Ligusticum mutellina* L.
Alpine Lovage

4–8 ins. Leaves bi-tripinnate, with linear-lanceolate leaflets. Umbels with 10–15 umbellets, but without any involucre. Flowers white or rose. Damp meadows, from about 4500–8400 ft. 6–8.

Ligusticum mutellinoides Crantz
Small Alpine Lovage

2–4 ins. Similar to the above, but with 12–20 umbellets, and with an involucre of 5–10 leaves. Flowers reddish, and greenish-white later. Prefers a non-limy soil and is found up to about 9000 ft. 7–8.

3 *Laserpitium siler* L.
Siler

16–48 ins. Leaves tri-pinnate, glabrous, with leaflets lanceolate, and entire. Flowers white. Rocky limestone meadows, up to 6000 ft. 7–8. A lime-indicating plant.

4 *Laserpitium latifolium* L.
Broad-leaved Siler

24–60 ins. Similar to the above, but larger, with broadly oval, dentate leaves which are cordate at the base. Flowers white, with 20–30 umbellets. Limestone slopes, up to 6000 ft. 6–8. A lime-indicating plant.

5 *Molopospermum peloponesiacum* (L.) Koch.
Striped Hemlock
M. cicutarium DC.

24–48 ins. An imposing plant, with wide spread of fern-like leaves, wheel-like verticel of side umbels, and huge, 15–40 rayed, terminal umbel, is mainly to be found in the rocky limestone meadows of the southern Alps, up to about 6000 ft. 5–8.

6 *Orlaya grandiflora* L.
Large-flowered Orlaya

4–28 ins. Umbels with 5–8 rays. Outer petals of the external ray florets much enlarged. Found in limy or clay soil, up to about 3000 ft. 6–7.

1

2

3

4

5

6

Plate 55

PYROLACEAE

SECTION I. FLOWERS SOLITARY

1 *Moneses uniflora* L.
One-flowered Wintergreen
Pyrola uniflora L.

2–4 ins. Leaves sub-orbicular, in ground rosette. Flower stems leafless, bearing single, white, nodding flowers. Woods, locally abundant. 1800–6000 ft. 6–8.

SECTION II. STEM LEAFY. FLOWERS IN UNILATERAL SPIKE

2 *Orthilia secunda* L.
Serrated Wintergreen
Pyrola secunda L.

4–8 ins. Leaves oval, pointed, with saw-toothed edges. Flowers white, in unilateral spike, drooping at first, but erect in seed. Woods. Local. 2400–6000 ft. 6–7.

SECTION III. LEAVES SHORTER THAN THEIR PETIOLES. STYLE PROTRUDING. STAMENS ARCHING TO FORM A CLUSTER ABOVE THE OVARY

3 *Pyrola rotundifolia* L.
Greater Wintergreen

6–12 ins. Leaves sub-orbicular-obtuse, in basal rosettes. Flowers white, tinged pink, and sweetly scented, borne in a multilateral spike. Sepals acuminate, noticeably longer than broad. Widespread, in damp woods, and amongst scrubland. 0–6000 ft. 6–9.

4 *Pyrola chlorantha* Sw.
Green-flowered Wintergreen
P. virens Schweig.

4–12 ins. Leaves sub-orbicular-emarginate, in basal rosette. Flowers greenish-white, borne in a narrow, few-flowered spike. Sepals triangular, almost as broad as long. Very local, and mainly under Scots Pines, up to about 6000 ft. 6–7.

SECTION IV. LEAVES LONGER THAN THEIR PETIOLES. STAMENS IN A RING ROUND THE OVARY

5 *Pyrola minor* L.
Lesser or **Common Wintergreen**

4–8 ins. Leaves sub-orbicular-elliptic, in ground rosette. Flowers white, in a few-flowered, multilateral spike. Sepals triangular, about as broad as long. Style short, straight and not protruding. Local. Damp woods and scrubland, up to 7500 ft. 6–8.

Pyrola media Sw.
Medium Wintergreen

4–10 ins. Leaves sub-orbicular-oval in ground rosette. Flowers white, in a few-flowered, multilateral spike. Style thickening towards the tip, obliquely set, and slightly protruding. Local in woods and scrubland, up to 6000 ft. 6–8.

MONOTROPACEAE

6 *Monotropa hypopitys* L.
Yellow Bird's Nest
Hypopitys multiflora Scop.

4–10 ins. A leafless saprophyte, related to the Pyrolas. Plant yellowish-white. Flowers drooping in bud, arching in flower, and erect in seed. Local. In the humus, in damp long-standing woodland, up to over 5000 ft. 7–8.

1

2

3

4

5

6

Plate 56

ERICACEAE

1   *Rhododendron hirsutum* L.
   Hairy Alpenrose

Leaves ciliate, green on both sides. Flowers rose, rarely white. Limestone slopes, up to 6000 ft. 6–8.

2   *Rhododendron ferrugineum* L.
   Rusty Alpenrose

Similar to the above, but with stiffer leaves, not ciliate at the edge, and with old leaves rusty brown below. Flowers rose, rarely white. Favours a non-limy soil, and is widespread, up to well over 7000 ft. 7–8.

3   *Loiseleuria procumbens* L.
   Creeping Azalea
   Azalea procumbens L.

A prostrate sub-shrub. Leaves small, oval, turning crimson in autumn. Flowers small, rose, in 2–5 flowered umbels. Widespread, on lime-free slopes from 5400–8400 ft. 6–8.

4   *Rhodothamnus chamaecistus* L.
   Ground Cistus

4–10 ins. Leaves lanceolate, evergreen. Flowers rosy-pink, borne, 1–2, on long pedicels, at the tips of the stems. Confined to the dolomitic limestone of the eastern Alps, and the Bergamasque Alps. 6–7.

5   *Erica carnea* L.
   Alpine Heath

6–20 ins. Flowers rose, in unilateral spike. Locally abundant, on limestone slopes. 3–7.

6   *Calluna vulgaris* L.
   Ling, Heather

Common on lime-free soil, up to 7500 ft. 7–9.

1

2

3

4

5

6

Plate 57

ERICACEAE (continued)

1 *Arctostaphylos uva-ursi* L.
Bearberry

12–40 ins. A trailing sub-shrub. Leaves thick, leathery, entire, with edges not rolled inwards, as in *Vaccinium vitis-idaea*. Evergreen. Flowers flask-shape, pale rose to white. Berries red. No preference as to soil. Widespread, up to about 7500 ft. 4–6.

Arctostaphylos alpina (L.) Spreng.
Alpine or **Black Bearberry**
Arctous alpinus (L.) Nied.

6–12 ins. Leaves dark green, reticulate, turning crimson in autumn, and deciduous. Flowers white with greenish throat. Berry black. Limestone slopes, from 5700–7500 ft. 5–6.

Vaccinium vitis-idaea L.
Cowberry,
Red Whortleberry

4–12 ins. Leaves stiff, dark green, with edges rolled inwards, and punctate on their lower surface. Flowers white or rose, bell-shape, borne in close clusters. Berries red. In mountain woods and on humus, up to about 9000 ft. 5–7.

2a *Vaccinium myrtillus* L.
Whortleberry, Bilberry,
Huckleberry, Blaeberry

6–20 ins. Leaves yellowish-green. Berries black, and mealy. Common, on damp, non-limy soil, up to 7500 ft. 4–6.

2b *Vaccinium uliginosum* L.
Bog Whortleberry

6–28 ins. Differs from the above in the blue-green undersides of the leaves, and the blue-black, rather than black, berries. Berries more mealy, and flowering period slightly later. 5–6.

3 *Vaccinium oxycoccus*
Cranberry
Oxycoccus quadripetalus Gilib.,
O. palustris Pers.

4–12 ins. Leaves small, oval, pointed, blue-green underneath. Flowers nodding, borne on long pedicels. Petals rose, up-turning. Berry red. Local, in sphagnum moss-covered bogs, up to about 6000 ft. 5–7.

EMPETRACEAE

4 *Empetrum nigrum* L.
Crowberry

4–18 ins. A trailing sub-shrub, with small, linear, leaves. Flowers rose, born in the axils of the leaves. Berry black. Damp rocks and heathland, from about 4000 ft to over 8000 ft. 5–6.

SOLANACEAE

Atropa belladonna L.
Deadly Nightshade

24–60 ins. Stem sturdy, erect and arching at the tip. Leaves large, broadly oval. Flowers large, bell-shaped, dingy violet, borne 1–3 in the axils of the leaves. Berries shiny black, when ripe, and as large as a small cherry. Extremely poisonous. Local, in shady and bushy places, mainly on limestone, and up to about 4800 ft. 6–8.

RUTACEAE

5 *Dictamnus albus* L.
Burning Bush, Dittany,
Fraxinella

24–48 ins. Upper stem glandular, cinnamon scented. Leaves pinnate. Flowers with 5 ragged, rose, petals. (Illustration shows plant in seed.) Very local on dry, bushy limestone slopes, up to about 3600 ft. 5–6.

OXALIDACEAE

6 *Oxalis acetosella* L.
Wood Sorrel

2–6 ins. Usually white, the illustration shows the uncommon pink form. This widespread woodland plant may be found, in the Alps, up to about 6000 ft. 4–6.

1   2a   2b

3   4

5   6

Plate 58

PRIMULACEAE

1 *Primula auricula* L.
Auricula

4–10 ins. Leaves oboval, grey-green often very mealy. Flowers scented, golden-yellow, with mealy gorge and calyx. Limestone rocks, from 3000–7500 ft. 5–7.

2 *Primula elatior* L.
Oxlip

4–10 ins. Flowers sulphur-yellow, darker at the gorge. Widespread, up to about 6600 ft. 3–6.

3 *Primula farinosa* L.
Bird's Eye Primula

2–8 ins. Leaves mealy below. Flowers rosy-lilac to purple, occasionally white. Widespread. Damp limestone meadows, up to 7500 ft. 5–8.

4 *Primula longiflora* All.
Long-flowered Primula
P. halleri J. F. Gmelin

4–10 ins. Similar to the above, but taller. Flowers larger, and corolla tube much longer, but few flowers per head. Damp limestone meadows, mainly in the southern Alps, from 3000–8700 ft. 6–7.

5 *Primula viscosa* All.
Viscid Primula
P. latifolia Lapeyr.

2–4 ins. Leaves obovate, glandular hairy on both sides. Flower stems longer than the leaves. Flowers violet-purple, all turning to one side. Gorge the same colour as the rest of the flower. Damp, lime-free rocks, mainly in the eastern Alps. In Switzerland, only in the Grisons. From 6600–8000 ft. 4–7.

Primula pedemontana Thomas
Piedmont Primula

2–5 ins. Leaves not viscid, but glabrous, green underneath, dentate to crenulate, with edges margined with hairs, tipped by reddish glands. Flowers violet-purple, borne 2–10 on stems about twice as long as the leaves. Local. Savoy, Piedmont and west Alps. 6–7.

6 *Primula hirsuta* All.
Hairy Primula

1–3 ins. Leaves glandular-hairy, with clearly notched edges. Flower stem not longer than the leaves. Flowers rosy-violet, with paler eye, borne 1–7 per stem. Damp, lime-free rocks, in the central and southern Alps, from 4500–8400 ft. 4–7.

Primula daonensis Leybold
Val di Daone Primula
P. oenensis Thomas

1–3 ins. Differs from *P. hirsuta* in having narrower leaves, flower stem longer than the leaves, which are covered with orange to dark-red glands, instead of colourless to orange, as in the above. Flowers rosy-violet. Local and confined to Italian-Swiss frontier, Val di Daone, Ortler Alps, Tonale and Mustair. 6–7.

1
2
3

4
5
6

Plate 59

PRIMULACEAE (*continued*)

1   *Primula × berninae* Kerner
    Bernina Primula

A natural hybrid between *P. hirsuta* and *P. viscosa*, see Plate 58, which is to be seen on the Bernina Pass, where these two Primulas may be seen together in quantity as well as *P. integrifolia*. 6–7.

2   *Primula integrifolia* L.
    Entire-leaved Primula

1–2½ ins. Leaves small and entire. Flowers rosy-lilac, with deeply notched petals, borne, 1–3 per head, on short stems. Damp rocks, and snow valleys, mainly in the eastern Alps. In Switzerland, only to the east of the Lauterbrunnental. From 6000–7800 ft. 5–8.

    Primula tirolensis Schott
    Tyrolean Primula

1½–2 ins. Leaves small, roundly obovate, dentate and very glandular hairy. Flowers rose, borne singly or in pairs, on short stems. Local, mainly in the Dolomites. 6–7.

3   *Primula minima* L.
    Dwarf Primula

1–2 ins. Leaves small, spatulate, with comb-like teeth at the tip, in tight rosettes. Flowers large, rose with paler eye, borne singly, as a rule, on very short stems. Petals narrow at the base, deeply notched, and with widely divergent tips. On lime-free soil, in the Tyrol, Dolomites, and eastern Alps. Not in Switzerland, or in France. 6–7.

4   *Primula glutinosa* Wulfen
    Glutinous Primula

1–3 ins. Leaves spatulate, glutinous and toothed round the tips. Flowers violet-blue, borne 1–7 per stem, in tightly compact heads. Screes and snow valleys in the central and eastern Alps, east of Arosa. 7–8.

5   *Primula marginata* Curtis
    Margined Primula

1–3 ins. Leaves obovate, with deeply dentate edges, which are whitely mealy. Flowers violet to rose. Very local, in the Maritime Alps, on limestone rocks exposed to the north and up to about 6000 ft. 5–7.

    Primula allionii Loisel.
    Allioni's Primula

1–2½ ins. Leaves oblong, entire, covered with white glandular hairs. Flowers bright rose to violet-rose, borne solitary, as a rule, on pedicels without visible stems. Rare. In the Ligurian and Maritime Alps. 3–5.

6   *Primula spectabilis* Tratt.
    Benacensis Primula

2–4 ins. Leaves grass green, glandular, oval-elliptic. Flowers bright rose to light violet, deeply notched, and with widely divergent tips. Very local, on the limestone mountains near L. Garda.

    ssp. *glaucescens* Moretti
    Bergamasque Primula

Between L. Idro and L. Como, this Primula is represented by the ssp. *glaucescens* with stiffly cartilaginous edges to the leaves.

    ssp. *clusiana* Tausch.
    Clusius Primula

In the Austrian limestone Alps, *P. spectabilis* is represented by the ssp. *clusiana*.

1

2

3

4

5

6

Plate 60

PRIMULACEAE (*continued*)

1 *Soldanella minima* Hoppe
   Least Soldanella

2–4 ins. Leaves orbicular. Flowers solitary, white to pale violet. South eastern limestone Alps. Not in Switzerland. From 4500–7500 ft. 5–7.

2 *Soldanella alpina* L.
   Alpine Soldanella

2–6 ins. Leaves reniform, dark green and shiny. Flowers bluish-violet occasionally white, borne 1–3 per stem. Petals translucent, deeply fringed Found on limestone and flowers as the snow recedes, from 3600–8400 ft. 4–7.

3 *Soldanella pusilla* Baumg.
   Lesser Soldanella

1–4 ins. Rather similar to the above, but with flowers more narrowly bell shaped, less deeply fringed, rosy-violet, streaked purple inside, and born solitary, or in pairs. In the Swiss Alps, east of the Simplon Pass. French and Italian Alps. Lime-free soil, from 5400–8400 ft. 5–8.

4 *Douglasia vitaliana* L.
   Yellow Androsace
   Gregoria vitaliana Duby,
   Aretia vitaliana Murray

2–8 ins. Plant loosely trailing. Leaves in tight rosettes. Flowers bright golden-yellow. Local, on rocky slopes. Abundant on the Simplon Pass. 6–8.

ANDROSACE SUB-DIVISION CHAMAEJASME

5 *Androsace chamaejasme* Wulfen
   Rock Jasmine

1–4 ins. Leaves ciliate at the edge. Flower stem longly hairy. Flowers white fading to rose. Limestone meadows, up to 9000 ft. 6–7.

6 *Androsace obtusifolia* All.
   Blunt-leaved Rock Jasmine

2–4 ins. Leaves oboval to lanceolate, slightly ciliate at the edge. Stem sparsely hairy. Flowers white, with yellow eye. Very similar to the above, but found on lime-free soil, from 5400–8400 ft. 6–8.

1

2

3

4

5

6

Plate 61

PRIMULACEAE (*continued*)

SUB-DIVISION CHAMAEJASME (*continued*)

1 *Androsace carnea* L.
Flesh-pink Rock Jasmine

2–4 ins. Small ground rosettes of lanceolate leaves. Flowers flesh pink, with yellow gorge. Local. Lime-free soil. Southern and western Alps. Vaud and Valais, in Switzerland, and in the Maritime Alps in France. From 5400–8400 ft. 6–7.

2 *Androsace lactea* L.
Milk-white Rock Jasmine

2–8 ins. Leaves linear-lanceolate, in compact rosettes. Flowers large, white, with yellow eye, and clearly notched petals, borne singly, or in loose umbels, on leafless stems. Local, in the southern and western limestone Alps, up to about 6000 ft. 6–8.

SUB-DIVISION ARETIA

3 *Androsace alpina* (L.) Lam.
Alpine Androsace
A. glacialis Hoppe

1–2 ins. Leaves small, covered with whitish, stellate hairs, forming a loose cushion of neat rosettes. Flowers pink, or white, borne on very short pedicels. Local. Lime-free moraines and screes, of the central and southern Alps, from 6200–9000 ft. 7–8 or 9.

Androsace helvetica (L.) All.
Swiss Androsace

Plant forming tight, almost hemispherical mats of moss-like rosettes. Flowers sessile, white, with yellow eye. Limestone cliffs, in the Savoy, and Swiss Alps, but on non-limy rocks, in the Dauphine. Local from 6000–9000 ft. 5–8.

Androsace imbricata Lam.
Vandelli's Androsace
A. vandellii Turra,
Aretia multiflora Moretti,
A. argentea Lois.

Plant forming dense, whitely-tomentose mats. Flowers white, with a red eye, borne on short pedicels. Local. On the lime-free rocks of the central and southern Alps, from 6000–9000 ft. 7–8.

Androsace pubescens DC.
Downy Androsace

1–2 ins. Plant forming nearly flat, ash-green mats. Leaves with simple or forked hairs. Flowers white, with yellow gorge, borne on short pedicels. Local. Limestone screes in the northern and western Alps. 6–7.

4 *Cyclamen europaeum* auct.
European Cyclamen
C. purpurascens Mill.

2–6 ins. Leaves sub-orbicular-reniform. Flowers rose, sweetly scented, with gorge entire. Mountain woods, plentiful in places, especially in the southern Alps. 6–9.

5 *Cyclamen neapolitanum* Ten.
Sowbread, Neapolitan Cyclamen
C. hederifolium Ait.

4–8 ins. Leaves sub-triangular, cordate at the base, brightly marbled with light and dark green and wavy at the edges. Flowers rose, occasionally white, not scented, with gorge dentate, and flowering slightly before the leaves are fully developed. Mountain woods, rare in Switzerland. 8–10.

PLUMBAGINACEAE

6 *Armeria alpina* DC.
Alpine Thrift
Statice montana Mill.

4-8 ins. Leaves narrowly linear. Flowers rosy-lilac. Lime-free meadows. Mainly in the southern Alps, rare in Switzerland, from 6600–8400 ft. 7.

Plate 62

GENTIANACEAE

1 *Gentiana lutea* L.
   Yellow Gentian

20–50 ins. Leaves large, broadly elliptic, opposite, in pairs. Flowers large, starry, golden-yellow, borne in verticels, in the axils of the leaves. When not in flower, this plant should not be mistaken for *Veratrum*, Plate 1, which has its leaves alternate, instead of opposite. Locally abundant, in limestone meadows, up to about 7500 ft. 7–8.

2 *Gentiana purpurea* L.
   Purple Gentian

8–24 ins. Leaves oval, green. Flowers large, erect, purple, with yellowish centre. Calyx divided into 2 lobes, simulating a spathe. Meadows on rather lime-poor soil, in the western Alps, eastwards to Landeck, in Tyrol. From 4800–6900 ft. 7–9.

Gentiana pannonica Scop.
Hungarian Gentian

Similar to *G. purpurea*, but with calyx divided into 5–6 lobes, leaves more elliptic in shape, and flowers dull purplish-violet, spotted blackish-purple, and not yellowish inside. An eastern Alpine, with its western limit at Churfisten, in Switzerland. 7–9.

3 *Gentiana punctata* L.
   Spotted Gentian

8–24 ins. Leaves oval-oblong. Flowers yellowish, usually spotted purplish-brown. Calyx in 5–6 lobes. Prefers non-limy soil, and is widespread, in rocky meadows, up to about 7500 ft. 7–8.

4 *Gentiana germanica* Willd.
   German Felwort or
   Gentian
   Gentianella germanica Willd.

A collective species, with varying local forms, and summer and autumn races, some of which are difficult of recognition. All of them, however, have flowers of 5 petals, and are bearded at the gorge. 5–7, 6–9 or 8–10, according to sub-species.

5 *Gentiana tenella* Rothb.
   Slender Gentian

2–4 ins. Stem branching from the base. Flowers small, pale violet, with 4 petals and bearded at the gorge. Flowers borne singly, on long pedicels. Local. Damp, non-limy meadows, up to 7500 ft. 7–8.

6 *Gentianella campestris* L.
   Meadow Gentian, Field Felwort
   Gentiana campestris L.

2–8 ins. Flowers violet to white, with 4 petals, bearded at the gorge. Calyx with 4 lobes, 2 much broader than the others. Mainly on limestone. Common up to 7500 ft. 5–10.

1

2

3

4

5

6

Plate 63

GENTIANACEAE (*continued*)

1 *Gentiana nivalis* L.
Snow or **Small Alpine Gentian**

1–6 ins. Stem usually branching, and leaves elliptic-lanceolate. Calyx sub-cylindrical, slightly winged. Flowers small, dark blue. Local. Poor ground, from 5000–8000 ft. 7–8.

2 *Gentiana utriculosa* L.
Bladder Gentian

3–12 ins. Stem usually branching from the base. Leaves oval to oblong. Calyx ovoid, broadly winged, and much inflated after flowering. Flowers dark blue. Local, in damp or swampy places, from the plains, up to nearly 7000 ft. 5–8.

3 *Gentiana pneumonanthe* L.
Marsh Gentian

6–24 ins. Leaves small, linear-lanceolate, in pairs. Flowers dark blue, with 5 paler streaks in the corolla tube, and spotted green inside. Local, mainly in meadows, which are swampy in the spring, but dry in summer. Not in bogs as the name suggests. Found up to about 4500 ft. 8–10.

4 *Gentiana asclepiadea* L.
Willow Gentian

10–40 ins. Leaves oval-lanceolate, in pairs. Flowers brilliant blue, with gorge spotted purple, and with paler streaks in the corolla tube. The plant is sometimes erect, with flowers and leaves all round the stem, and sometimes arching, with leaves and flowers in the same plane. Local. Limestone woods and scrubland, up to about 6000 ft. 8–10.

COLLECTIVE SPECIES OF *GENTIANA ACAULIS*

5 *Gentiana clusii* Perr. & Song.
Stemless Gentian

2–4 ins. Leaves elliptic-lanceolate, pointed, and with marked central nerve. Flowers almost stemless, large, deeply bell-shaped, and brilliant blue. Calyx with lobes acuminate, meeting at an acute angle at the base, and with tips applied to the corolla tube. Common on limestone meadows, from 6000–7800 ft, but at lower altitudes on the Jura. 5–8.

forma *caulescens*

G. clusii has a long-stemmed variety, found in the southern Alps, which should not be confused with *G. angustifolia* below.

6 *Gentiana kochiana* Perr. & Song.
Koch's Stemless Gentian
G. latifolia Jakow.

2–4 ins. Similar to the above, but with leaves wider, pale green and multi-nerved. Flowers dark blue, flecked green inside. Calyx with lobes not applied to the corolla tube, narrowing at the base, where they are separated by a whitish, papery, sinus. Common, on lime-free soil, from 3600–8400 ft. 6–8.

Gentiana angustifolia Vill.
Gentianella
G. acaulis L.

2–5 ins. Plant stoloniferous. Leaves long and narrowly lanceolate. Flowers borne on a visible stem. Dark blue. Calyx lobes not applied to the corolla tube, and separated by a blunt sinus. Limestone meadows. French Alps. 5–8. The *Gentiana acaulis* of Horticulture.

Plate 64

GENTIANACEAE (*continued*)

1 *Gentiana ciliata* L. **Fringed Gentian**
4–12 ins. Flowers blue to violet-blue, with 4 lobes in the form of a cross, and with fringed edges. Widespread. On limy meadows, in the latter part of the summer, up to 6000 ft. 8–10.

2 *Gentiana bavarica* L. **Bavarian Gentian**
2–8 ins. Leaves oboval-roundish, the lower ones often smaller than the higher ones. Stem with 3–4 pairs of blunt-ended leaves. Calyx slightly winged. Flowers intensely dark blue. Damp meadows and beside streams from 5400–9000 ft. 7–8.

3 var. *imbricata* Schl. **Schleicher's Gentian**
At the higher elevations, *G. bavarica* becomes known as *G. imbricata*. Flower stem much reduced in length, and with lower leaves closely overlapping and simulating a rosette.

4 *Gentiana verna* L. **Spring Gentian**
1½–4 ins. Lower leaves elliptic, to elliptic-lanceolate, forming a true rosette with the largest leaves at the base. Flowers brilliant blue, occasionally white, with spatulate petals, between which are 2, erect, white streaked appendages. Flowers as the snow recedes, and common, from 2400–9000 ft. 3–8.

5 *Gentiana orbicularis* Schur. **Favrat's Gentian** G. favratii Rittener
An uncommon form of *G. verna*, with leaves shorter, more rounded, and with lobes of the corolla orbicular, and even wider than long. Strictly local, on limestone slopes, from 6000 to over 8000 ft. 7–8.

6 *Gentiana brachyphylla* Vill. **Short-leaved Gentian**
1½–2½ ins. Another form of *G. verna*, with leaves soft, roundish-oval, pointed at the tip. Flowers with long, narrow, corolla tube, and narrow, unwinged calyx. Poor, non-limy ground, in the central and southern Alps, from 5700–9000 ft and even to 12,000 ft. Local. 7–8.

Plate 65

GENTIANACEAE (*continued*)

1 *Swertia perennis* L.
Marsh Felwort

6–16 ins. Ground leaves bluntly elliptic, on long petioles. Stem leaves sessile. Flowers dull violet, starry, borne on pedicels arising from the axils of the upper leaves, and forming a tapering spike. Local. Damp meadows, in the lower Alpine regions, from about 2100–5400 ft. 7–8.

APOCYNACEAE

2 *Vinca minor* L.
Lesser Periwinkle

6–12 ins. Trailing. Leaves opposite, evergreen. Flowers blue, violet, rose or white. Woods. Widespread. 4–5.

Vinca major L.
Greater Periwinkle

Not considered to be wild in the Alps.

ASCLEPIADACEAE

3 *Vincetoxicum officinale* Moench.
Vincetoxicum

12–36 ins. Stem erect, with leaves oblong-lanceolate, opposite, in pairs. Flowers small, 5-petalled, yellowish-white, borne in small, umbel-like cymes, in the axils of the leaves. Seedpods sickle-shaped and pendant. Infusions of this plant are said to have been used, at one time, for poisoning the tips of arrows. Locally abundant, on bushy slopes, usually on limestone. 6–8.

POLEMONIACEAE

4 *Polemonium coeruleum* L.
Jacob's Ladder

12–36 ins. This well-known garden plant may be found wild, or naturalised, in various parts of the Alps, mainly on limy soil, from 2400–6600 ft. 6–8.

BORAGINACEAE

5 *Pulmonaria officinalis* L.
Lungwort

6–12 ins. This well-known garden plant may be found flowering in the alpine woods, from early spring, until mid-June. It has two forms, one with leaves very clearly spotted, as illustrated, and one with leaves unspotted, or only faintly spotted. The latter form is the one most usually found.

6 *Pulmonaria angustifolia* L.
Narrow-leaved Lungwort
P. longifolia Bastard

Similar to the above, but with narrow, unspotted leaves and bright blue flowers. Local, in the Valais, Tessin, Grisons and in the French and Italian Alps. 4–6.

Plate 66

BORAGINACEAE (*continued*)

1 *Anchusa italica* Retz.
Italian Alkanet
A. azurea Mill.

A tall-growing plant, with hairy stem and leaves. Flowers bright blue, purple in bud. Waysides, mainly in the south-eastern Alps. 5–9.

Anchusa officinalis L.
Common Alkanet

This plant with purplish flowers is also common by the waysides.

2 *Lithospermum purpureo-coeruleum* L.
Blue Gromwell

6–12 ins. Leaves lanceolate, hairy. Flowers large, dark blue, purple in bud, borne in a terminal head. Local. Sunny, and stony slopes, in the southern Alps, up to about 2400 ft. 4–5.

3 *Borago officinalis* L.
Borage

Stem and leaves hairy. Flowers bright blue, with petals almost reflexed. Waste ground, up to about 3300 ft. 5–6.

4 *Echium vulgare* L.
Viper's Bugloss

This common plant, with its roughly hairy stem and leaves, and its bright blue flowers, which are red in bud, is a feature of the roadsides, and river gravels, up to about 6000 ft. 5–10.

5 *Symphytum tuberosum* L.
Tuberous Comfrey

8–20 ins. Leaves hairy, only very slightly decurrent on the stem. Flowers yellow. Stamens alternating with pointed scales, which are shorter than the corolla tube. Damp woods, and meadows, up to 4500 ft. 3–6.

6 *Myosotis alpestris* F. W. Schmidt
Alpine Forget-me-not

2–6 ins. Plant dwarf. Flowers bright blue. Found up to over 8000 ft. 6–7.

Plate 67

BORAGINACEAE (*continued*)

1   *Eritrichium nanum* All.
King of the Alps

1–2 ins. Leaves silvery haired. Flowers large, brilliant sky-blue, with yellow eye. The plant forms tiny cushions in the clefts of lime-free rocks, on humus-collecting shelves, and even in short turf. Local, in the French Alps, and in Switzerland, in the Valais–Binntal, Simplon and Zermatt areas, and in the Grisons, from 7500–9000 ft. 7–8.

2   *Cerinthe glabra* Mill.
Hairless Cerinthe
C. alpina Kit.

12–18 ins. Leaves glabrous, embracing the stem, and blue-green below. Flowers tubular, yellow, with bases purple, arising from the axils of the leaves, and forming a nodding head of flowers. Local. Limestone meadows and woods, from 3000–5400 ft. 6–8.

LABIATAE

3   *Scutellaria alpina* L.
Alpine Skullcap

8–16 ins. Stems trailing. Leaves oval, crenulate. Flowers large, with bluish violet over-lip, and paler under-lip. Local. Limestone screes of the western Alps, eastwards only to Zermatt. 7–8.

4   *Calamintha alpina* (L.) Lam.
Alpine Savory
Satureja alpina L.

4–12 ins. Trailing, with ascendant stems. Aromatic. Leaves dentate. Flowers violet, on separate pedicels, arising from the axils of the leaves. Widespread from 2400–6900 ft. 6–8.

5   *Thymus serpyllum* L.
Wild Thyme

A collective species, with many variants. Flowers rose to purple. Plant strongly aromatic. Widespread, up to over 9000 ft. 4–9.

6   *Ajuga pyramidalis* L.
Pyramidal Bugle

4–8 ins. Stem unbranched, pyramidal. Flower head quadrangular. Flowers violet-blue to whitish. Leaves often washed purple. Found up to over 7000 ft. 6–8.

1

2

3

4

5

6

Plate 68

LABIATAE (*continued*)

1   *Ajuga reptans* L.
    Bugle

4–12 ins. This plant is common from the plains up to the lower Alpine regions. Flowers violet-blue, occasionally white. 4–8.

2   *Prunella grandiflora* L.
    Large-flowered or
    Greater Self-heal

2–16 ins. Leaves oblong-oval. Flowers rich violet-purple, occasionally white, and borne in a compact terminal head. Widespread. 6–10.

3   *Origanum vulgare* L.
    Marjoram

12–20 ins. Stem erect. Leaves oval, entire, or slightly toothed. Flowers rose to purple. Widespread, on limy soil. 7–9.

4   *Teucrium montanum* L.
    Mountain Germander

4–10 ins. Stem almost woody at the base. Leaves small, lanceolate, entire, grey tomentose underneath. Flowers yellowish-white. Local. Limestone rocks, and screes in warm and sheltered places, from about 2400–6600 ft. 6–8.

5   *Teucrium chamaedrys* L.
    Wall Germander

Plant slightly woody at the base. Leaves rather stiff, and deeply crenulate at the edges. Flowers rose. Locally abundant. Rocky places. 6–8.

6   *Mentha longifolia* L.
    Horse Mint

12–40 ins. Leaves greyish-green, and downy. Flowers pale violet, to dull rose, in dense, lateral and terminal spikes. Widespread, in damp places. 7–9.

1

2

3

4

5

6

Plate 69

LABIATAE (*continued*)

1   *Horminum pyrenaicum* L.
Pyrenean Dead Nettle

4–8 ins. Stem unbranching. Leaves sub-orbicular to oval, with deeply reticulate veining, and crenulate edges. Flowers large, violet-blue, occasionally white, borne in a unilateral spike. Tessin and Grisons only, in Switzerland, but common in the southern Alps. 6–8.

2   *Salvia glutinosa* L.
Jupiter's Distaff

16–48 ins. Plant glandular-sticky in its upper half. Leaves broadly spear-shaped and dentate. Flowers large, sulphur-yellow. Widespread, in mountain woods. 6–8.

3   *Salvia pratensis* L.
Meadow Clary

12–32 ins. Leaves oval-oblong, cordate at the base. Flowers bright blue to purplish. Widespread. 5–9.

4   *Dracocephalum ruyschianum* L.
Ruysch's Dragon's Head

4–12 ins. Leaves linear-lanceolate, entire, with edges inrolling. Flowers large, strongly bluish-violet, in a tight terminal head. Very local, in light woods, and dry meadows, from about 4200 to 6000 ft. 7–8.

    Dracocephalum austriacum L.
Southern Dragon's Head

6–12 ins. Similar to the above, but with stem woolly, leaves either simple, or deeply pinnate, with linear, entire, segments, inrolling at the edges. Flowers very dark. and intense, violet, over 1 in in length. Dry meadows at about the limit of cultivation. Rare in Switzerland–Valais and Lower Engadine, but also to be found in the French Alps, from Mt Cenis to Provence, and in the Val Venosta. 5–6.

5   *Melittis melissophyllum* L.
Bastard Balm

8–20 ins. Leaves oval, cordate at the base. Flowers large, purplish, white and rose or white. Widespread, in woods, 6–7.

6   *Stachys densiflora* Benth.
Dense-flowered Betony
Betonica hirsuta L.

4–12 ins. Leaves oval-oblong, cordate at the base, and crenulate at the edges. Flowers purple, in a dense, terminal head. Local, in the west and south. 7.

1 2 3

4 5 6

Plate 70

SCROPHULARIACEAE
MULLEINS WITH FILAMENTS OF THE STAMENS FURNISHED WITH VIOLET OR PURPLE HAIRS

1 *Verbascum blattaria* L. **Moth Mullein**
20–40 ins. Leaves glabrous, wavy-toothed at their edges, the lower ones oblong, and the upper ones sessile, and slightly cordate at the base. Flowers yellow, or very occasionally white, washed violet, borne singly on easily visible pedicels, in loose spikes. Local. 6–8.

2 *Verbascum nigrum* L. **Dark Mullein**
12–40 ins. Upper part of stem angular. Leaves oblong-oval, nearly glabrous on their upper surface, and slightly dentate. Upper leaves sessile, and lower leaves petiolate, and inclined to be cordate at the base. Flowers yellow, occasionally white, borne in tight groups, on visible pedicels, in a tall, compact spike. Widespread. 6–8.

Verbascum chaixii Vill. **Nettle-leaved Mullein**
16–40 ins. Differs, from the above, in having cylindrical stem, leaves rarely cordate at the base, shorter pedicels to the flowers, which are violet at the gorge, instead of purple. Uncommon. 7–8.

MULLEINS WITH FILAMENTS OF THE STAMENS FURNISHED WITH WHITE HAIRS

SECTION I. LEAVES NOT DECURRENT

3 *Verbascum lychnitis* L. **White Mullein**
24–56 ins. Stem very angular. Leaves shortly tomentose below, and slightly dentate. Upper leaves sessile. Flowers small, clear yellow or white. Widespread. 6–9.

4 *Verbascum pulverulentum* Vill. **Hoary Mullein**
24–50 ins. Stem cylindrical. Plant covered with a white, blanket-like tomentum, which is easily rubbed off, and is a distinguishing characteristic. Upper leaves half embracing the stem. Flowers yellow, or white. Rough ground, mainly in the south and west. 7–9.

SECTION II. LEAVES MORE OR LESS DECURRENT

i. Flowers concave, with 2 long filaments four times as long as the anthers

5 *Verbascum thapsus* L. **Aaron's Rod, Common Mullein**
12–72 ins. Leaves oblong-elliptic, decurrent the whole length of the internode, and with greyish tomentum on both sides. Flowers yellow. Widespread. 7–9.

6 *Verbascum crassifolium* DC. **Thick-leaved Mullein** V. montanum Schrad.
16–60 ins. Leaves oblong-elliptic, decurrent to just over half the internode, and with a yellowish tomentum on both sides. Flowers yellow, occasionally white. Widespread, but less common than the above. 6–9.

1

2

3

4

5

6

Plate 71

SCROPHULARIACEAE (*continued*)

SECTION II. LEAVES MORE OR LESS DECURRENT

ii. Flowers not concave. Stamens with 2 long filaments twice as long as the anthers

1 *Verbascum thapsiforme* Schrad.
Dense-headed Mullein

20–80 ins. Leaves oblong-elliptic, decurrent the whole length of the internode, and with greyish-yellow tomentum. Flowers clear yellow, rarely white. Waste ground. Widespread. 7–9.

2 *Verbascum phlomoides* Schrad.
Woolly Mullein

20–60 ins. Leaves oblong-elliptic, decurrent just over half the length of the internode, and with yellowish tomentum. Flowers very large, and clear yellow. Local, mainly in the south. 7–9.

3 *Digitalis grandiflora* Mill.
Yellow Foxglove
D. ambigua Murray

12–28 ins. Flowers yellow, spotted brown inside. Widespread. 6–8.

4 *Digitalis lutea* L.
Straw Foxglove

20–40 ins. Somewhat similar to the above, but with smaller, tightly tubular flowers, not spotted brown inside, and borne in a close unilateral spike. Also widespread. 6–8.

5 *Melampyrum nemorosum* L.
Bush Cow-wheat

8–24 ins. Leaves oval to oval-lanceolate. Flower yellow, with orange hood, and violet-purple bracts. Damp, and shady places. Local. 6–8.

6 *Melampyrum silvaticum* L.
Wood Cow-wheat

Leaves narrowly lanceolate. Flowers yellow, slightly drooping. Woods. Common, but mainly in the mountains. 6–8.

Melampyrum pratense L.
Field or **Common Cow-wheat**

Similar to the above, but with broader leaves, and flowers nearly erect. Common. 6–9.

1   2   3

4   5   6

Plate 72

SCROPHULARIACEAE (*continued*)

1 *Veronica bellidioides* L.
Daisy-leaved Speedwell

2–6 ins. Ground leaves in daisy-like rosette. Stem leaves in pairs. Flowers dark blue, in a terminal head. Local, on lime-free soil, from about 5400 to over 8000 ft. 6–8.

2 *Veronica spicata* L.
Spiked Speedwell

5–14 ins. Leaves lanceolate, dentate at the edges. Flowers dark blue, in a dense, and rigid, terminal spike. Local, in sunny places, from the valleys up to about 6000 ft. 7–9.

3 *Veronica alpina* L.
Alpine Speedwell

2–4 ins. No basal rosette of leaves. Leaves oval to sub-orbicular, increasing in size towards the top of the stem. Flowers blue, in a tight, terminal head. Meadows and snow valleys, from about 4500–9000 ft. 6–8.

4 *Veronica latifolia* L.
Broad-leaved Speedwell

12–28 ins. Stem erect, hairy. Leaves rather nettle-shaped. Flowers pale rose to pale violet, in loose spikes, arising from the axils of the leaves. Woods. Common. 5–8.

5 *Veronica teucrium* L.
Germander Speedwell

8–20 ins. Leaves mostly sessile, strongly dentate. Flowers blue, in long axillary spikes. Calyx with 5 lobes, 1 being smaller than the others. Local. 6–7.

6 *Veronica officinalis* L.
**Common Speedwell,
Swiss Tea**

4–12 ins. Trailing. Flowers pale lilac, or pale blue, with darker veining. Flower spikes arising from the axils of the leaves. The leaves were used for making tea. Woods. 5–8.

1

2

3

4

5

6

Plate 73

SCROPHULARIACEAE (*continued*)

1   *Veronica aphylla* L.
Leafless-stemmed Speedwell

$1\frac{1}{2}$–$2\frac{1}{2}$ ins. Leaves all in ground rosettes. Stem leafless, bearing 2–5 lilac flowers. Local on limestone rocks and meadows, from about 4800–8000 ft. 6–8.

2   *Veronica fruticans* Jacq.
Rock Speedwell
V. saxatilis Scop.

2–8 ins. Leaves oblong to elliptic. Flowers intensely blue, borne in few-flowered heads. Widespread, from about 3000–7800 ft. 6–8.

SUB-DIVISION PAEDEROTA

3   *Veronica bonarota* (L.) Wetts.
Buonarota's Speedwell
Paederota bonarota L.

4–8 ins. Leaves large, hairy, deeply and irregularly notched, and increasing in size towards the top of the stem. Flowers violet-blue, with long pointed petals, and long corolla tube, and borne in an arching, terminal spray. Italian Alps. 7–8.

4   *Veronica lutea* (Scop.) Wetts.
Yellow Speedwell
Paederota lutea Scop.

Closely related to the above, and somewhat similar, but with yellow flowers. South-east Alps. 6–8.

5   *Linaria alpina* L.
Alpine Toadflax

1–2 ins. Trailing. Flowers rich violet, with orange at the gorge, when on limestone, and without the orange gorge, when on non-limy soil. Widespread. 6–8.

6   *Erinus alpinus* L.
Alpine Erinus

2–8 ins. Leaves spatulate, dentate at the tip. Flowers purplish-violet. Limestone rocks. Plentiful in places, but absent in others. 6–7.

Plate 74

SCROPHULARIACEAE (*continued*)

1 *Bartsia alpina* L.
Alpine Bartsia

4–10 ins. Stem simple. Leaves oval, bluntly toothed, and tinted dark violet. Flowers brownish-violet. Anthers with white hair. Damp mountain meadows. Widespread. 6–8.

2 *Euphrasia rostkoviana* Hayne
Large-flowered Sticky Eyebright

2–6 ins. Upper part of the stem branching, with short internodes. Flowers usually white, with upper lip violet, and lower lip spotted yellow, and veined violet. An autumnal race of Eyebrights, common up to 7500 ft. 7–10.

3 *Euphrasia minima* Jacq.
Little Kneeling Eyebright

1–5 ins. Stem usually unbranched. Flowers very variable, yellow, white or purplish-violet. 7–9.

4 *Rhinanthus alectorolophus* Scop.
Greater Yellow Rattle

8–16 ins. Stem green. Flowers yellow, in a large head, with yellowish bracts. A summer flowering race. Widespread, up to about 7500 ft. 5–7.

Rhinanthus angustifolius Gmelin
Lesser Yellow Rattle

4–12 ins. Stem streaked black. Leaves narrow and longer than the numerous short internodes. Flowers yellow. An autumnal race. Widespread. 6–9.

ssp. *subalpinus* Sterneck
Sub-alpine Rattle

Not quite so tall-growing, and with leaves shorter than the fewer, more widely spaced internodes. A summer race. Widespread. 7–8.

LOUSEWORTS WITHOUT A BEAK ON THE UPPER LIP

YELLOW, BEAKLESS LOUSEWORTS

i. Upper lip with two lateral teeth under the tip

5 *Pedicularis comosa* L.
Bearded Lousewort

8–16 ins. Stem erect. Flowers pale yellow, in a longish, compact, head. Calyx inflated, with pointed teeth, wider than long. Very local. Meadows, and banks, mainly in the southern and western Alps. 6–8.

ii. Upper lip without lateral teeth

6 *Pedicularis foliosa* L.
Leafy Lousewort

8–20 ins. Stem stoutly erect. Flower head large, dense and interspersed with longly projecting leaves. Flowers pale yellow. Grassy, limestone slopes. 6–8.

Pedicularis oederi Vahl.
Oeder's Lousewort

2–4 ins. Leaves with crenulate segments. Flowers yellow, with upper lip tipped reddish-brown. Local, on limestone, in the north and west. 7.

Plate 75

SCROPHULARIACEAE (*continued*)

RED, BEAKLESS LOUSEWORTS

i. Upper lip with two lateral teeth under the tip

1 *Pedicularis palustris* L. **Marsh Lousewort, Red Rattle** — 8–16 ins. Plant with, usually, only 1 branching stem. Flowers purple, in the axils of the leaves, and in a terminal head. Marshy meadows. 5–7.

2 *Pedicularis sylvatica* L. **Wood Lousewort** — 4–8 ins. Plant branching from the base, and with several flowering stems, the central one flowering almost from the base. Flowers rose, in few-flowered heads. Local. Mountain woods. 5–6.

ii. Upper lip without lateral teeth

3 *Pedicularis verticillata* L. **Verticillate Lousewort** — 2–6 ins. Stem leaves 3–4, arranged in a verticel. Flowers purple, in a dense blunt, head. Limestone meadows. 6–8.

4 *Pedicularis rosea* Wulfen. **Rosy Lousewort** — 3–6 ins. Stem nearly leafless. Calyx hairy, with 5 entire, triangular teeth. Flowers rose, with darker upper lip, borne, almost sessile, in a short, compact head. Local, on non-limy ground, in the southern and south-eastern Alps not in Switzerland. 6–7.

Pedicularis recucita — See Plate 76.

YELLOW, BEAKED LOUSEWORTS

5 *Pedicularis tuberosa* L. **Tuberous Lousewort** — 4–8 ins. Calyx hairy, with foliose teeth. Flowers pale yellow, in a short dense, head. Locally abundant, on non-limy soil. 7–8.

6 *Pedicularis elongata* Kerner **Long-headed Lousewort** — 8–16 ins. Calyx hairless. Flowers pale yellow in a long, narrow, spike. Limestone meadows of the south and west. Local. 7–8.

1   2   3

4   5   6

Plate 76

SCROPHULARIACEAE (continued)

1 *Pedicularis recucita* L.
Rust-red Lousewort

8–16 ins. Stems robust, with alternate leaves, often tinted purple. Flowers rusty-purple, yellowing at the base, and borne in a dense, blunt head. Flowers without beak. Colour unique. Locally abundant, on damp ground, up to about 7500 ft. 7–8.

RED, BEAKED LOUSEWORTS

2 *Pedicularis rostrato-spicata* Crantz
Spiked Beaked Lousewort
P. incarnata Jacq.

8–16 ins. Stem hairless below the flower head. Calyx hairy, with triangular teeth. Supporting bracts with 3 lanceolate-entire lobes. Flowers bright rose, with darker beak, borne in a dense, narrow spike. Very local, on lime-free soil, in the south and west. 7–8.

Pedicularis cenisia Gaudin
Mt Cenis Lousewort

4–8 ins. Stem ascendant, bearing 4–10 flowers in a short, compact head. Flowers rose, with beak purple. Calyx with 4 foliose lobes and 1 narrow, pointed lobe, the whole white-woolly. French Alps, between 4500–7500 ft. 7–8.

Pedicularis asplenifolia Flörke
Fern-leaved Lousewort

4 ins. Flowers rose, with darker beak and borne on pedicels as long as the calyx tube. Calyx with 5 crenulate lobes, the whole covered with reddish hairs. Local, in the eastern Alps, Dolomites and in the Lower Engadine. 7–8.

3 *Pedicularis gyroflexa* Vill.
Oblique Beaked Lousewort

6–10 ins. Stem and leaves downy. Calyx woolly with long foliose teeth. Flowers large, bright rose, borne in a loose spike. Local, on limestone meadows, in the south and west. 6–7.

4 *Pedicularis kerneri* Dalla Torre
Kerner's Lousewort
P. rhaetica Kerner

2–6 ins. Leaves purplish, mainly in ground rosette. Stems weakly ascendant. Calyx tubular, tapering towards the base. Flowers large, clear purple, and with hairless lower lip, borne 1–3 at the tips of the stems. Local, on lime-free soil, up to over 9000 ft. 6–9.

5 *Pedicularis rostrato-capitata* Crantz
Capitate Beaked Lousewort

3–8 ins. Leaves alternate. Calyx bell-shaped, glabrous, or ciliate only on the nerves. Flowers clear purple, with lower lip ciliate at the edge, borne in compact, few-flowered heads, at the tips of the stems. Local, on limestone meadows of the eastern Alps, and in the Grisons and St Gallen, only, in Switzerland. 7–8.

6 *Orobanche hederae* Duby
Ivy Broomrape

One of a Family of parasitic plants, difficult of recognition, owing to their ability to parasitise a plant from a considerable distance. Some of them live on a single host plant, as does *O. hederae* on ivy, and others on groups of plants. It is not possible, in this book, to deal fully with this family.

1

2

3

4

5

6

Plate 77

LENTIBULARIACEAE

All the Butterworts are insectivorous. When an insect is caught on the sticky surface of the leaves, the edges of the leaf curl inwards to enfold and absorb it. The leaves are sometimes used for making Junket.

1 *Pinguicula alpina* L.
Alpine Bog Violet or
Butterwort

2–6 ins. All leaves in ground rosette, glutinous. Flowers white, with underlip spotted orange-yellow at the throat. Local, in damp places, on limestone, up to 6600 ft. 5–7.

2 *Pinguicula vulgaris* L.
Common Butterwort

2–8 ins. Rather similar to the above, but bluish-violet, tinged orange at the throat. Common, on damp ground up to nearly 7000 ft. 5–7.

3 ssp. *leptoceras* Rchb.
Hairy-spurred Butterwort

Large flowers, spotted white on the lower petals. Damp rocks, and boggy ground. Local. 5–7.

GLOBULARIACEAE

4 *Globularia nudicaulis* L.
**Leafless-stemmed
Globularia**

4–10 ins. Leaves large, spatulate, in ground rosette. Stem leafless. Flowers large, pale blue. Locally abundant often in company with *Erica carnea*, on limestone slopes. Up to nearly 7000 ft. 6–8.

5 *Globularia elongata* Hegetsch.
Common Globularia

4–10 ins. Flower stem very leafy. Flowers blue. Common, on dry ground, mainly at the lower levels. 4–6.

6 *Globularia cordifolia* L.
Shrubby Globularia

A trailing sub-shrub, carpeting limestone rocks and rocky slopes. Leaves obovate, emarginate or tridentate at the tip. Flowers grey-blue on leafless stems. Locally abundant. 5–7.

1

2

4

3

5

6

Plate 78

CAPRIFOLIACEAE

1 *Lonicera coerulea* L.
Blue Honeysuckle

3–5 ft. A shrub. Leaves elliptic, bluntly tipped, and blue-green below. Flowers greenish-white, with 5 almost equal lobes, borne on pedicels shorter than the flowers. Flowers pendant. Berries blue-black, joined, in pairs throughout their length. Mountain woods. 5–6.

2 *Lonicera nigra* L.
Black Honeysuckle

24–50 ins. Leaves oblong-elliptic, downy at first, but glabrous below, later. Flowers in pairs, white or rosy, with 2 very prominent lobes, borne on pedicels three to four times as long as the flowers. Berries black, joined slightly at the base. Mountain woods. 5–6.

3 *Lonicera xylosteum* L.
Fly Honeysuckle

3–6 ft. Young shoots, pedicels, and the undersides of the leaves downy, at first. Flowers white, tinged rose and yellow, with 2 lobes considerably longer than the corolla tube, borne on ascendant pedicels, about 1 in long. Berries cherry-red, joined narrowly at the base. Widespread, up to about 5400 ft. 5.

4 *Lonicera alpigena* L.
Alpine Honeysuckle

24–60 ins. Leaves broadly elliptic, and longly acuminate, glabrous, when mature. Flowers brownish-red, with 2 lobes very prominent, borne, in pairs, on long pedicels. Berries cherry-red, wider than long, and joined at least two-thirds of their length. Mountain woods. 5–6.

5 *Linnaea borealis* L.
Woodland Linnaea

A trailing woodland plant, with roundish-oval leaves. Flower stems erect, leafless, bearing 1–3, nodding, bell-shaped, scented flowers, which are pale rose, streaked rosy violet inside. Very local, in mossy pine woods. In Switzerland, rarely found east of the Simplon. 7.

6 *Sambucus ebulus* L.
Danewort, Herbaceous Elder

24–60 ins. A tall growing plant, resembling the Common Elder, but without the woody stem. Flowers white, suffused rose. Locally abundant, in scrubland, and meadow, mainly in the mountains. 7–8.

1

3

2

4

5

6

Plate 79

RUBIACEAE

1 *Asperula cynanchica* L.
Squinancy-wort

4–16 ins. Stems branching, ascendant. Leaves linear, in whorls around the stem. Flowers small, pink, narrowly tubular and 4-lobed. Locally abundant on banks and in meadows. 6–8.

2 *Galium pumilum* Murray
Dwarf or **Slender Bedstraw**

1–4 ins. Trailing. Leaves narrow, in whorls around the stem. Flowers whitish. A variable species. Common, on limestone, up to 8400 ft. 7–8.

3 *Galium helveticum* Weig.
Swiss Bedstraw

1–4 ins. Trailing. Leaves oval-obtuse, in whorls of 6–8, glabrous. Flowers white to cream. Limestone screes, up to 9000 ft. 7–8.

VALERIANACEAE

Valeriana dioica L.
Lesser or **Dioecious Valerian**

4–16 ins. Plants dioecious, with male and female flowers on different plants. Male flowers large, rosy and female flowers small, white. Lower leaves oval, entire. Stem leaves with 5–9 segments. Damp places, up to over 5000 ft. 4–6.

4 *Valeriana tripteris* L.
Trifid Valerian

6–20 ins. Stem glabrous. Base leaves cordate. Stem leaves tripartite. Flowers white to pink in a wide corymb. Limestone gravels, up to 7800 ft. 6–8.

5 *Valeriana montana* L.
Mountain Valerian

4–16 ins. Rather similar to the above, but with leaves shiny instead of matt, rounded at the base, or even tapering to the petiole. Stem leaves oval, and entire. Limestone, from 3000–7800 ft. 5–7.

6 *Valeriana saxatilis* L.
Rock Valerian

4–12 ins. Ground leaves elliptic-lanceolate. Stem leaves small, linear. Flowers white, in a loose corymb. Limestone rocks of the southern and eastern Alps. 6–8.

Valeriana celtica L.
Spikenard, Spike

2–8 ins. Leaves glabrous, entire, oblong-lanceolate at the base, and linear on the stem. Flowers yellowish, tinted red outside, borne in small cymes, arranged in verticels around the upper stem, to form an interrupted spike. The Emperor Nero is said to have used the roots of this plant for scenting his bath. Local, on non-limy soil, in the high Alpine meadows, mainly in the southern Alps, between 6000–7400 ft. 7–8. Protected.

Plate 80

VALERIANACEAE (*continued*)

1 *Valeriana supina* Ard.
Eastern Dwarf Valerian

$1\frac{1}{2}$–4 ins. Leaves spoon-shaped to lanceolate, ciliate. Flowers pale rosy-lilac, borne in small, compact, heads. Local. Limestone screes of the eastern Alps, 5400–6800 ft. 7–8.

Valeriana saliunca All.
Western Dwarf Valerian

2–8 ins. Lower leaves oval to spatulate, tapering to the petiole, and glabrous. Upper leaves linear. Flowers pale rosy-lilac. Limestone screes of the western Alps. In Switzerland, only to the west of the St Gotthard. 7–8.

2 *Centranthus ruber* L.
Red Valerian

Native of southern Europe, and North Africa. Freely naturalised, mainly in the south. 5–8.

3 *Centranthus angustifolius* Mill.
Narrow-leaved Valerian

12–24 ins. Leaves linear, grey-green. Flowers rosy-pink. Mainly in the southern Alps. 6–8.

DIPSACACEAE

4 *Scabiosa lucida* Vill.
Glossy Scabious

4–12 ins. Stem usually unbranched, bearing a single flower. Leaves pinnate, with very narrow segments. Flowers rosy-lilac. Widespread. 7–8.
There are several other species of *Scabiosa* to be found in the Alps.

5 *Knautia sylvatica* L.
Wood Scabious

8–40 ins. Stem branching. Leaves elliptic-lanceolate, opposite, entire or dentate. Flowers violet. Woods and mountain meadows. Common. 7–9.
There are several other species of *Knautia* to be found in the Alps.

6 *Cephalaria alpina* L.
Giant Scabious

24–50 ins. Stem leaves pinnate, with lanceolate segments, saw-toothed at the edge. Flowers large, pale yellow. Local to rare. 7–8.

Plate 81

CAMPANULACEAE

1 *Campanula thyrsoides* L.
Yellow Bellflower

4–20 ins. Stem erect. Leaves woolly. Flowers pale yellow, massed in a broad blunt, spike. Limestone meadows. 6–7.

Campanula petraea L.
Veronese Bellflower

12–16 ins. Leaves grey below and white-cottony above, oval-oblong, longly petiolate. Flowers palest yellow, with styles protruding, borne in tight terminal and smaller lateral heads, enfolded in involucres of bracts. Prefer limestone. Very local, in the Alps around L. Garda and in the Ligurian Alps. 8–9.

2 *Campanula spicata* L.
Spiked Bellflower

6–28 ins. Stem leafy, stoutly erect. Flowers bluish-violet, arising in groups from the axils of the leaves in a very long, narrowly tapering spike. Mainly on limestone, in the southern Alps. 7–8.

3 *Campanula glomerata* L.
Clustered Bellflower

10–24 ins. Plant glabrous, or downy. Leaves rounded or cordate at the base. Flowers violet-blue, massed in a compact head. Widespread. 6–8.

Campanula cervicaria L.
Hairy Clustered Bellflower

12–30 ins. Similar to the above, but with leaves tapering to the petiole, roughly hairy. Flowers pale blue, with longly protruding style. Rare in Switzerland. French and Italian Alps. 6–8.

4 *Campanula barbata* L.
Bearded Bellflower

4–12 ins. Flowers pale blue to white, nodding, bearded inside, and borne on stiffly erect stems, in a few-flowered, unilateral cluster. Calyx with a reflexed appendage between each lobe. Lime-free meadows. 6–8.

Campanula sibirica L.
Siberian Bellflower

Up to 2 ft. Stem stiff, and branching. Leaves oblong-lanceolate to linear. Flowers small, violet-blue, borne in a wide and ample panicle. Calyx with reflexed appendages between each lobe. Warm limestone slopes, in the south-eastern Alps (L. Garda area), not in France or Switzerland. Up to about 5400 ft. 6–8.

5 *Campanula rhomboidalis* L.
Rhomboid-leaved Bellflower

10–20 ins. Stem leafy. Lower leaves rhomboidal. Upper leaves oval, dentate. Flowers large, blue, borne in a loose, unilateral cluster. Widespread, in Alpine meadows, eastwards to the Hinterrheintal, from 3000–6600 ft. 6–8.

6 *Campanula scheuchzeri* Vill.
Scheuchzer's Bellflower

2–10 ins. Stems ascendant. Ground leaves lanceolate, and stem leaves linear. Flowers large, violet-blue, borne singly, or up to 5 per stem. Meadows. Widespread, between 4500–9000 ft. 7–9.

1   2   3

4   5   6

Plate 82

CAMPANULACEAE (*continued*)

1 *Campanula linifolia* Scop.
Flax-leaved Bellflower

4–16 ins. Ground leaves cordate. Stem leaves linear. Calyx with long, reflexed, filiform lobes. Flowers pale violet-blue, similar to the common Harebell, but narrower, and with more sharply pointed lobes. Local, Savoy and Italian Alps. 7–8.

2 *Campanula cochlearifolia* Lam.
Slender Bellflower
C. pusilla Hänke

2–6 ins. Leaves of ground rosette suborbicular. Stem leaves oval, to linear. Flowers clear blue, hemispherically bell-shaped, nodding, with lobes blunt and borne singly, or up to 5 per stem. Widespread. Limestone rocks, screes and sandy places, from about 2100–8000 ft. 7–8.

3 *Campanula cenisia* L.
Mt Cenis Bellflower

2 ins. Creeping. Leaves roundish to oval, in ground rosettes, and linear on the stem. Flower pale lilac-blue, with bells deeply cut into narrow pointed lobes. Local, on limestone screes in the French Alps, and in the Vaud, Valais and Bernese Oberland, in Switzerland. From about 7500–9000 ft. 7–9.

4 *Campanula excisa* Schle.
Stencilled Bellflower

2–6 ins. Leaves linear-lanceolate. Flowers pale blue-violet, the bells being waisted in the middle, with long, narrowly pointed lobes, and almost circular excisions between each lobe. Local, on lime-free soil, in the Savoy, the Tessin, and Valais (Simplon), from about 4300–8000 ft. 6–9.

5 *Campanula raineri* Perpenti
Rainer's Bellflower

2–4 ins. Leaves oblong-spatulate, faintly dentate. Flowers very large, erect, widely open, blue to violet-blue. Confined to the Alps, between L. Lugano and L. Garda. 7–8.

Campanula morettiana Rchb.
Moretti's Bellflower

In the Dolomites, its place is taken by *C. morettiana*, with flowers less widely open, and leaves roundish to sagittate.

6 *Campanula allionii* Vill.
Alpine or **Allioni's Bellflower**
C. alpestris All.

2–3 ins. Creeping. Leaves oval to lance-shaped, downy, grey-green. Flower very large, longly tubular, and rich violet-blue. Calyx with reflexed appendages between the lobes. Local to rare, and confined to the French Alps. 7–8.

Plate 83

CAMPANULACEAE (*continued*)

1 *Campanula trachelium* L.
Nettle-leaved Bellflower,
Bats-in-the-Belfry

20–40 ins. Stem sharply angular. Lower leaves cordate at the base, borne on long petioles, nettle-like in shape, and deeply doubly-dentate, at the edge Flowers large, ascendant, violet-blue. Common. 7–9.

2 *Campanula rapunculoides* L.
Creeping Bellflower

12–30 ins. Plant stoloniferous. Stem bluntly angular. Lower leaves cordate at the base. Upper leaves oval-lanceolate. Flowers bluish-violet, drooping, borne in a dense, unilateral spike. Widespread. 7–9.

3 *Campanula bononiensis* L.
Bolognese Bellflower

12–60 ins. Stem round, and downy. Lower leaves cordate at the base. Upper leaves oval-lanceolate, grey-green to grey tomentose below. Flowers violet-blue, in a serried spike, with each flower borne separately in the axils of a small bracteole. Rare, in the Savoy, Valais, Tessin and in the Italian Alps. 7.

4 *Campanula persicifolia* L.
Willow Bellflower

16–40 ins. Stems erect, bearing linear-lanceolate leaves. Flowers large, widely bell-shaped, blue, borne up to 6 per stem, in the axils of the upper leaves. Local, on waste ground, and in clearings. 6–7.

5 *Campanula patula* L.
Spreading Bellflower

12–28 ins. Leaves smooth, faintly crenulate. Stem slender, inclined to trail Flowers violet-blue, divided to about half the length of the corolla tube. with narrow, pointed, reflexed lobes, and borne in a loose corymb-like panicle. Woods and banks, up to over 4000 ft. 6–8.

6 *Campanula rapunculus* L.
Rampion, Ramps

12–36 ins. Stem erect. Ground leaves oblong-oval, tapering to the petiole Flowers blue, with lobes about a third of the length of the corolla tube, and borne in a long, narrow, raceme-like panicle. Widespread. 5–7.

1　　　　　　　　　　　　　　　2　　　　　　　　　　　　　　　3

4　　　　　　　　　　　　　　　5　　　　　　　　　　　　　　　6

Plate 84

CAMPANULACEAE (*continued*)

1   *Phyteuma globularifolium*
Sternb. & Hoppe
**Globularia-leaved
Rampion**

$1-2\frac{1}{2}$ ins. Leaves of ground rosette oboval to spatulate, often tridentate Flowers blue, borne 5–7 in tight hemispherical heads. Bracts oval. Local Lime-free meadows and rocks, from 6000–9000 ft. 7–8.

2   *Phyteuma orbiculare* L.
Round-headed Rampion

4–20 ins. Ground leaves cordate to lanceolate, with edges crenulate. Bract oval to triangular, acuminate, and shorter than the flowers, which are dark blue, and borne in an almost orbicular head. Tips of buds incurving before opening. Limestone meadows. Widespread, up to 7500 ft. 5–7.

3   *Phyteuma scheuchzeri* All.
Scheuchzer's Rampion

4–18 ins. Lower leaves and upper leaves with saw-toothed edges. Flower blue, with their tips straight, when in bud, borne in an almost spherical head. Bracts linear, longly acuminate and often reflexed, much longer than the flowers. Rocks and rocky places, mainly in the southern Alps. 5–7.

4   *Phyteuma spicatum* L.
Spiked Rampion

12–30 ins. Leaves oval-acuminate, about as wide as long, borne on long petioles. Stem leaves narrower, and all with doubly-dentate edges. Flower yellowish-white, in a dense, tapering spike. Widespread, in woods and shady places, up to 6300 ft. 5–8.
A blue-flowered form of this plant occurs in the Savoy and southern Alps

5   *Phyteuma ovatum* Honck.
Haller's Rampion
P. halleri All.

16–36 ins. Ground leaves triangular-cordate, about as wide as long, and upper leaves narrower, oval to oval-lanceolate, all with deeply doubly dentate edges. Flowers rich blackish-violet, in massive oval heads. Locally abundant, in meadows, between 3600–660 ft. 6–7.

  Phyteuma michelii All.
6   ssp. *betonicifolium* Vill.
Betony-leaved Rampion
P. betonicifolium Vill.
ssp. *scorzonerifolium* Vill.
**Scorzonera-leaved
Rampion**
P. scorzonerifolium Vill.

10–28 ins. Ground leaves oval-lanceolate, acuminate, with base cordate edges crenulate, and borne on long petioles. Flowers bluish-violet, in a dense, narrow spike. Flowers with 3 stigmas as a rule. Common, on lime free soil, from about 3000–7500 ft. 6–9.
12–36 ins. Very similar to the above, but with ground leaves sub-sessile linear, tapering to the base. Flowers clear lilac, usually with only 2 stigmas Confined to the southern Alps. 6–7.

1

2

3

4

5

6

Plate 85

CAMPANULACEAE (*continued*)

1 *Phyteuma hemisphericum* L.
Hemispherical-headed Rampion

$1\frac{1}{2}$–12 ins. Leaves linear, entire or dentate. Flowers dark violet-blue, borne in many-flowered hemispherical heads. Bracts oval-acuminate, shorter than the flowers. Widespread, on lime-free soil, up to over 9000 ft. 7–8.

2 *Phyteuma carestiae* auct.
Hedrianthus-leaved Rampion
P. hedrianthifolium R. Schutz.

1–6 ins. Leaves linear, with widely-spaced teeth at their edges. Flowers blue. Bracts linear-acuminate, the outer ones reflexed, and longer than the flowers. Rare. South-eastern Alps, and in the Grisons, in Switzerland. From 5400–9000 ft. 7–8.

3 *Phyteuma comosum* L.
Bearded Rampion

2–5 ins. Leaves roundish to oval, with wavy long-toothed edges, often grey-green and stiffly encrusted with lime. Flowerheads large for the size of the plant, borne on stems little taller than the leaves. Flowers broadly flask-shaped, whitish, tinged bluish-violet at the base, and longly tapering to blackish-purple tips. Stigmas protruding. This exceptionally beautiful plant is a native of the southern limestone Alps, from Mt Grigna eastwards to L. Garda and the Dolomites, and grows in the crevices of the dolomitic rocks. 7–8.

COMPOSITAE

4 *Leontopodium alpinum* Cass.
Edelweiss

2–8 ins. Plant intensely white-tomentose. Lower leaves spatulate. Upper leaves linear. Stem simple, bearing 2–10 small flowerheads, compactly arranged and bordered by a fringe of white-woolly leaves. Locally plentiful, on limestone, up to over 10,000 ft. 7–8.

5 *Erigeron alpinus* L.
Alpine Fleabane

2–16 ins. Stem single-flowered, or with several flowers. Differs from the Asters in having more than 1 row of ray florets. The colour varies from clear rose to purplish-violet. Meadows, from 4500–7800 ft. 7–9.

6 *Erigeron uniflorus* L.
One-flowered Fleabane

1–6 ins. Stem nearly always single-flowered. Calyx woolly haired, which is not the case in *Erigeron alpinus*. Flowers lilac, pale rose or whitish. Meadows, up to 9000 ft. 7–9.

Plate 86

COMPOSITAE *(continued)*

1 *Aster alpinus* L.
Alpine Aster

2–8 ins. Stems ascendant, single-flowered. Flowers with disc florets yellow, and ray florets violet. Widespread. Limestone rocks and meadows, from 4200–8400 ft. 6–8.

2 *Aster amellus* L.
Sub-alpine Aster

6–16 ins. Stems erect, many-flowered. Flowers with ray florets bluish-violet. Widespread on dry banks and stony meadows, mainly on limy soil, and in the southern Alps, up to about 3000 ft. 7–9.

3 *Adenostyles glabra* Mill.
Hairless Adenostyles
A. alpina Bluff & Fingerhuth

12–24 ins. Leaves ash-green below, kidney- to heart-shaped and regularly dentate at the edges. Upper leaves on petioles, which are not winged at the base. Flowerheads plumose, composed of many small florets of 3–6 flowers. Lilac-purple. Widespread, on limestone screes, and in bushy places, between 2700–6900 ft. 7–8.

4 *Adenostyles alliariae* Gouan
Alliaria-leaved Adenostyles
A. albifrons Rchb.

20–60 ins. Leaves less stiff than the above, irregularly and double dentate, matt green on the upper side, and white-cottony below, or glabrous below, and the same colour on both sides. Upper leaves either sessile, embracing the stem or on petioles winged at the base. Flowers lilac-purple, in large plumose heads. Widespread in woods and shady places, up to over 7000 ft. 6–9.

5 *Adenostyles leucophylla* Willd.
White-leaved Adenostyles

8–20 ins. Stem simple. Leaves triangular-cordate, very whitely tomentose below, and sometimes above, not regularly dentate. Bracts of the involucre tomentose. Flowers rosy, with 10–25 florets per head, in a many-headed, composite plume. Very local, on non-limy screes, up to over 8000 ft. 7–8.

6 *Homogyne alpina* L.
Alpine Coltsfoot

6–12 ins. Leaves reniform, dark green and shiny. Stems nearly leafless, bearing single heads of dull reddish-violet flowers. Common from 3800–8400 ft. 6–8.

1

2

3

4

5

6

Plate 87

COMPOSITAE (*continued*)

1 *Petasites paradoxus* Retz.
Glacial Butterbur
P. niveus Baumg.

Leaves triangular, cordate at the base. Lower sides white-tomentose. Composite flowerhead, grouped in a loose ovoid spike. Flowers pale rose. Damp stony places, up to 6600 ft. 3–7.

2 *Petasites albus* L.
White Butterbur
Tussilago alba L.

6–12 ins. Leaves roundish-cordate, unevenly dentate, and lower side with non-persistent grey tomentum. Base of the leaf, adjoining the petiole not edged by a strong nerve, as in the above. Flowers yellowish-white, in a roundish head, which lengthens with age. Damp woods, up to 5700 ft. 4–6.

3 *Tussilago farfara* L.
Coltsfoot

This common garden weed, which flowers before the leaves appear in earliest spring, may be seen, in full flower, as late as early August, on the cols of some of the high alpine passes. 2–8.

4 *Solidago virga-aurea* L.
Golden Rod

4–36 ins. Common on waysides, stony slopes and screes, from the plains up to 7500 ft. 7–10.

5 *Bellidastrum michelii* Cass.
False Daisy

4–10 ins. Leaves oblong-oboval, deeply dentate, and borne on long petioles. Flowers with the ray florets white, turning pinkish with age. Damp, and shady places. Common. 5–7.

6 *Chrysanthemum alpinum* L.
Alpine Moon Daisy

Plant dwarf, with flower stems ascendant. Leaves small, pinnate, with 3–11, finely cut lobes. Ray florets white. Bracts of the involucre edged dark brown. Widespread, on lime-free soil, up to over 7000 ft. 7–8.

Chrysanthemum leucanthemum L.
Moon Daisy, Marguerite, Ox-eye Daisy

A variable species, but larger than the above, in every way. Leaves dentate, rather than pinnate, and with the bracts of the involucre edged black, instead of brown. Limestone meadows, up to over 7000 ft. 5–9.

1   2   3

4   5   6

Plate 88

COMPOSITAE (*continued*)

1   *Achillea tomentosa* L.
Yellow Milfoil

4–8 ins. Leaves woolly, pinnate with linear segments. Flowers with both disc and ray florets golden-yellow. Local, on dry banks. In the Valais, in Switzerland. 5–7.

2   *Achillea moschata* Wulfen
Musk Milfoil

4–10 ins. Plant with aromatic scent. Leaves pinnate, with narrow, comb-like divisions, which are usually entire. Flowers white, in a simple corymb and with the bracts of the involucre bordered brown. Common in the central Alps, on lime-free soil, from 5000 to 9000 ft. 7–8.

3   *Achillea atrata* L.
Dark Milfoil

Plant not aromatic. Leaves pinnate, to bi-pinnate. Bracts of the involucre bordered black. Otherwise very similar to the above, but on limy soil in the central and eastern Alps, between 5000–7800 ft. 7–8.

4   *Achillea nana* L.
Dwarf Milfoil

2–4 ins. Plant grey-woolly. Leaves narrowly pinnate, feathery and strongly aromatic. Local, on lime-free soil, between 5400–9000 ft. 7–8.

5   *Achillea clavenae* L.
Claven's Milfoil

4–12 ins. Leaves silvery-grey, finely silky, pinnate, but with only a few wide, blunt segments. Local. Southern and eastern Alps and Dolomites. 7–8.

     Achillea millefolium L.
Milfoil, Yarrow

6–24 ins. Leaves very feathery. Flowers white or pink. Very common, from the plains to 7500 ft. 6–9.

6   *Achillea macrophylla* L.
Large-leaved Milfoil

20–40 ins. Leaves glabrous, irregularly pinnate. Flowers white, in a compound corymb. Widespread, in woods, and shady places, between 2700–6000 ft. 7–8.

     Achillea oxyloba DC.
Chamomile-like Milfoil
Anthemis alpina L.

6–12 ins. Leaves grey, feathery, with very fine segments. Stem with flowers merged into a single flowerhead, resembling a Marguerite. Found in the Dolomites and south-eastern Alps. Not in Switzerland. 6–7.

1 2 3

4 5 6

Plate 89

COMPOSITAE (*continued*)

1 *Antennaria dioica* (L.) Gaertn. **Cat's-foot** Gnaphalium dioicum L.

2–10 ins. Plant stoloniferous. Lower leaves spatulate, green or blue-green above and white tomentose below. Upper leaves linear. Bracts of the female flowers pink, and those of the hermaphrodite flowers white. Widespread, on poor dry ground, up to over 9000 ft. 5–7.

2 *Antennaria carpatica* Wahlenb. **Carpathian Cat's-foot**

2–8 ins. Plant not stoloniferous. Leaves with woolly tomentum on both sides. Bracts of the involucre brown. Local, on stony pastures and on humus, from about 4500–9000 ft. 7–8.

3 *Gnaphalium sylvaticum* L. **Wood Cudweed**

6–20 ins. Leaves tomentose, linear-lanceolate, decreasing in size from bottom to top. Flowers yellow, with bracts of the involucre brown, borne in the axils of the leaves, in a long narrow spike. Widespread, up to 7500 ft. 6–8.

4 *Gnaphalium supinum* Cass. **Dwarf** or **Creeping Cudweed**

1–4 ins. Plant woolly. Leaves linear to linear-lanceolate. Inflorescence erect, composed of 2–6 flowerheads, grouped tightly together. The outer bracts of the involucre are more than half the length of the flowerhead. Non-limy screes and snow valleys, from about 4800–9000 ft. 7–8.

Gnaphalium hoppeanum Koch **Hoppe's Cudweed**

1–4 ins. Similar to the above, but even more tomentose. Inflorescence nodding, not erect and with brownish bracts, of which the outer ones are between a third and one half as long as the flowerhead. Limestone meadows and screes, from about 6000–8400 ft. 7–8.

5 *Artemisia laxa* Fritsch **Loose** or **Loose-headed Wormwood** A. muttelina Vill.

2–6 ins. Plant silvery-grey and hairy. Leaves palmate. Flowers yellow, arranged in a loose spike. Flowerheads hairy. Bracts narrowly edged brown. Local. Moraines and screes, from about 5700–8400 ft. 7–8.

6 *Artemisia glacialis* L. **Glacial Wormwood**

2–6 ins. Plant very hairy and very aromatic. Leaves palmate, with 5, 3-lobed segments. Flowers golden-yellow, grouped in a tight head at the tip of the stem. Flower glabrous. Bracts white-cottony, edged brown. Rocks, in the western Alps. Local, up to over 9000 ft. 7–8.

Artemisia genipii Weber **Genepy**

2–6 ins. Plant silvery-grey. Lower leaves pinnate, or very deeply dentate. Flower stems ascendant, with the flowers in a narrow, unilateral, spike drooping at the tip, but erect, later. Flowers yellow, with blackish bracts. Local, on screes and moraines, from about 7500–9000 ft. 7–8.

1

2

3

4

5

6

Plate 90

COMPOSITAE (*continued*)

1 *Carduus nutans* L.
Nodding or **Musk Thistle**

12–40 ins. Leaves irregularly pinnate, and intensely spiny. Stem spini? winged. Flowers large, nodding, purple, with bracts of the involucre r? flexed and spiny. Common, up to 7500 ft. 7–8.

2 *Carduus defloratus* L.
Smooth-stemmed Thistle

12–32 ins. Leaves lanceolate, softly spiny at the edges. Upper part of ste? smooth. Flowers medium-sized, purple, borne singly. Widespread. Rock slopes, up to 9000 ft. 6–8.

3 *Carduus personatus* (L.) Jacq.
Great Marsh Thistle

24–72 ins. Lower leaves lyrate-pinnate. Upper leaves oval to oblong. Plan? not spiny. Flowers dark purple, borne in a tight terminal head. Widesprea? Damp mountain meadows, up to 6000 ft. 6–8.

4 *Cirsium spinosissimum* L.
Spiny Thistle

16–24 ins. As the name implies, this is the prickliest one of all, and is ? feature of the high alpine meadows, where it stands, immune from a? nibblers of herbage, bristling like a hedgehog. Widespread, from 540? 9000 ft. 7–8.

5 *Cirsium eriophorum* (L.) Scop.
Woolly Thistle
Carduus eriophorus L.

32–60 ins. Stem rigidly erect. Leaves stiff, intensely spiny. Flowers ve? large, bright purple. Widespread, on dry slopes, and in meadows, up ? over 6000 ft. 7–9.

6 *Cirsium oleraceum* (L.) Scop.
Yellow Meadow Thistle

20–60 ins. Plant erect, yellowish-green, and softly spiny. Leaves embraci? the stem. Flowers yellow, in compact heads, nestling in a saucer of protecti? leaves. Widespread. Damp meadows, up to 6000 ft. 6–9.

Cirsium heterophyllum

See Plate 92.

1

2

3

4

5

6

Plate 91

COMPOSITAE (*continued*)

1 *Cirsium eristhales* Jacq.
Yellow Woodland Thistle

32–60 ins. Leaves very deeply segmented, ciliate-spiny at the edge. Flowers yellow, nodding, borne at the tips of leafless stems. Local. Mountain woods up to 5400 ft. 7–8.

2 *Cirsium acaulon* (L.) Scop.
Ground or **Stemless Thistle**
Carduus acaulos L.

Leaves very spiny, in ground rosette. Flowers purple, usually practically stemless. Widespread. Mountain meadows, up to 6000 ft. 7–9.

3 *Carlina acaulis* L.
Carline Thistle

2–6 ins. Ground rosette of very spiny leaves. Flowers practically stemless, and up to 4 ins in diameter, including the white, ray-like bracts, which simulate the ray florets of other composites. Common on limy soil, from about 2400–7500 ft. 7–9.

var. *caulescens* DC.

The visibly stemmed variety of *C. acaulis*, which may often be seen in company with the type.

Carlina acanthifolia All.
Acanthus-leaved Carline Thistle

Plant stemless. Leaves sessile, white-tomentose below, and sometimes above, and with broader divisions than in the case of *C. acaulis*. Flowers between 5–7 ins in diameter, including the fringe of ray-like bracts, which are silvery-white to shining pale yellow. Southern Alps and Pyrenees, mainly on limestone, between 1500–5400 ft. 7–9.

4 *Centaurea cyanus* L.
Cornflower, Bluebottle

12–32 ins. Stems branching, to bear a single flower per stem. Common, from the plains, up to over 5000 ft. 6–10.

5 *Centaurea montana* L.
Mountain Knapweed

4–24 ins. Leaves elliptic to oblong-lanceolate, usually entire. Stems bearing a single flower, with centre reddish-purple, and ray florets blue. Common, up to nearly 6000 ft. 6–8.

6 *Centaurea scabiosa* L.
Great Knapweed

12–48 ins. Stem simple or branching. Leaves pinnate to bi-pinnate. Flowers large, purple, borne singly at the tips of the branches. Widespread, from the plains, up to 7800 ft. 7–8.

1

2

3

4

5

6

Plate 92

COMPOSITAE (*continued*)

1   *Centaurea uniflora* L.
One-flowered Knapweed

4–12 ins. Leaves entire, and intensely white-tomentose. Flowers large purple, 1 per stem. Western Alps, not in Switzerland, from 4500–7500 ft 7–8.

     Centaurea nervosa Willd.
One-flowered Knapweed

4–12 ins. Another form of the above but with leaves green to grey-green wavy-toothed at the edges. Widespread in alpine meadows, from 3600– 7800 ft. 7–8.

2   *Centaurea rhapontica* L.
Great Alpine Saw-wort
Rhaponticum scariosum Lam.

Leaves very large, oblong-oval, acuminate, often cordate at the base. Flowe stems up to 5 ft, bearing singly, enormous purple, thistle-like flowers. Bract of the involucre brown, scaly and reminiscent of a fir cone. Local, on rock limestone slopes between 4500–6300 ft. 7–8.

3   *Serratula tinctoria* L.
Saw-wort

12–40 ins. Leaves normally pinnate, with large terminal lobe, but occasionall entire, with saw-toothed edges. Stem leafy and branching. Flowers purple, i terminal heads or corymbs. Damp meadows, common in places, from 4000– 7000 ft. 7–9.

     Saussurea alpina (L.) DC.
Alpine Saw-wort
Serratula alpina L.

2–12 ins. Not to be confused with the above. Leaves lanceolate, slightl toothed, and grey web-felted underneath. Flowers violet-purple, in a tigh terminal head. Bernina. Windy places and screes, from about 5700–8400 ft 7–8.

     Saussurea discolor Willd.
Tomentose Alpine Saw-wort
Serratula discolor L.

6–12 ins. Lower leaves oval-oblong, truncate at the base, or even cordate and white-tomentose below. Flowers purple. Similar distribution, but les common, than *S. alpina*. Sella Pass and Gardena Pass in the Dolomites From 4500–8400 ft. 7–8.

4   *Cirsium heterophyllum* Hill
Melancholy Thistle
C. helenioides (L.) Hill

20–40 ins. Leaves of two sorts, either pinnate or entire, white-tomentos below. Flowers purple, borne singly, or 1–3 per head. Damp places. Locally abundant, from 3000–6000 ft. 7–8.

5   *Cicerbita alpina* (L.) Wallr.
Alpine Lettuce
Lactuca alpina (L.) A. Gray,
Mulgedium alpinum Less.

24–50 ins. Leaves lyrate-pinnate, with very large end segment. Flower bluish-violet, in a dense, blunt, spike. Widespread, in mountain woods, u to 6600 ft. 7–8.

6   *Lactuca perennis* L.
Perennial Prickly Lettuce

8–32 ins. Leaves blue-green, pinnate, with segments pointing backwards Flowers large, bluish. Common in some limestone districts, up to over 500c ft. 5–6.

1

2

4

5

6

Plate 93

COMPOSITAE (*continued*)

1 *Senecio alpinus* L.
Alpine Ragwort

12–50 ins. Leaves oval, dentate, cordate at the base and pointed at the tip. Flowers golden-yellow, in many-flowered heads. Meadows, mainly round farms and chalets, up to over 6000 ft. 7–8.

2 *Senecio fuchsii* Gmelin.
Fuch's Ragwort

24–60 ins. Leaves lanceolate, tapering to narrowly-winged petioles. Flowers golden-yellow, with rather sparse ray florets, giving the individual flowers a star-like appearance. Widespread in mountain woods, up to over 5000 ft. 7–9.

3 *Senecio abrotanifolius* L.
Orange Ragwort

6–16 ins. Leaves pinnate, very finely divided. Stem leafy, bearing a few large, bright orange to reddish-orange flowers. Local, in the central and southern Alps. In Switzerland, in the Grisons and Valais, westwards only to the Visp Valley. 7–9.

4 *Senecio incanus* L.
Downy Ragwort

2–6 ins. Leaves silvery, segmented halfway to the principal nerve. Flowers bright orange-yellow, in tight terminal heads. Found on stony ground, and to the west of a line drawn between Uri and the Tessin, from 6000–10,000 ft. 7–9.

5 ssp. *carniolicus* Willd.
Eastern Downy Ragwort

2–6 ins. Differing from the above in having grey-green leaves, divided less than halfway to the central nerve and in being found only to the east of the St Gotthard. 5700–9000 ft. 7–9.

6 *Senecio uniflorus* All.
One-flowered Ragwort

2–5 ins. Rather similar to *S. incanus* but with leaves much less deeply segmented, and with as a rule, only one, large, golden-yellow flower. Uncommon. On the Simplon Pass, it may be seen in company with *S. incanus*. On stony, lime-free ground, from 6600–10,000 ft. 7–9.

Senecio doronicum L.

See Plate 95.

1

2

3

4

5

6

Plate 94

COMPOSITAE (*continued*)

Tragopogon pratensis L.
Goat's Beard, Jack-go-to-bed-at-noon
1 ssp. *orientalis* (L.) Vollm.

12–24 ins. The form of *T. pratensis* most likely to be seen in the Alps is the sub-species *orientalis*, with larger flowers than the type, in which the ray florets are only about as long as the bracts of the involucre.
In the sub-species, the rays are much longer than the bracts. Widespread, in meadows, up to about 6000 ft. 5–6.

2 *Hypochoeris uniflora* Vill.
One-flowered Cat's Ear

6–16 ins. Leaves lanceolate, in ground rosettes. Stem stoutly erect, much thickened immediately below the flowerhead. Flowers large, golden-yellow. Local. Mountain meadows, from about 5000–7500 ft. 7–8.

3 *Crepis aurea* L.
Orange-red Hawk's Beard

2–12 ins. Leaves oboval to oblong, and hairless. Stem leafless, bearing only 1 orange-red flower. Common, in meadows from about 3600–8000 ft. 5–9. There are many other species of *Crepis* to be found in the Alps.

4 *Aposeris foetida* (L.) Less.
Stinking Aposeris

4–8 ins. Easily recognised by its neat rosettes of leaves, with their curious, deep, triangular indentations and its habitat in deep woodland shade. Flowers golden-yellow, borne singly, on slender stems, which droop as the flowers fade. Locally abundant, on limy soil, mainly in the southern Alps, between about 2400–6000 ft. 6–7.

5 *Scorzonera aristata* Ramond
Awned Scorzonera, Black Salsify

Up to 20 ins. Leaves narrow, erect and grass-like. Stems single-flowered. Flowers golden-yellow. Meadows and waysides of the southern and south-eastern Alps, up to about 7000 ft. 7–8.

Scorzonera purpurea L.
6 ssp. *rosea* Waldst. & Kit.
Rosy Scorzonera

Up to 24 ins. Leaves grass-like. Stems single-flowered. Flowers sugar-cake pink, up to 2 ins in diameter. South-eastern Alps, up to 6000 ft. 6–8.

1

2

3

4

5

6

Plate 95

COMPOSITAE (*continued*)

1 *Senecio doronicum* L.
Doronicum Ragwort

8–20 ins. Plant greyish-green. Leaves alternate, oval to lanceolate, longly acuminate, with edges dentate, and surfaces slightly tomentose. Stem erect, cottony, bearing 1–3 large, golden-yellow, daisy-like flowers, each being borne solitary, at the tips of branches. Limy soil, from about 4500–7800 ft. 7–8.
This plant is shown here because of its resemblance to *Arnica* and *Doronicum*.

2 *Arnica montana* L.
Mountain Arnica

8–16 ins. Plant aromatic. Ground leaves opposite, in pairs, in a neat rosette. 1–2 pairs of opposite leaves per stem. Flowers large, golden-yellow, daisy-like, borne 1–3 per stem. Widespread, on lime-free soil, from about 2400–7800 ft. 6–8.

3 *Doronicum grandiflorum* Lam.
Doronicum

6–16 ins. Leaves alternate, not opposite, as above, oval inclined to cordate at the base, hairy but not tomentose, and with edges wavily toothed. Upper leaves sessile, embracing the stem, which bears only 1, large, golden-yellow, daisy-like flower. Limestone debris, from about 5700–8400 ft. 7–8.

4 *Doronicum clusii* All.
Clusius' Doronicum

2–12 ins. Rather similar to the above, but with leaves tapering to the petiole, not cordate, and stem leaves not embracing the stem. Rare in the north. Widespread, on lime-free soil, in the central and southern Alps, from about 6000–8400 ft. 7–8.

5 *Doronicum cordatum* Sch.-Bip.
Heart-leaved Doronicum
D. columnae Ten.

6–24 ins. Ground leaves reniform, and rather small. Flowers also rather small, usually borne singly, on a long slender stem. South-eastern Alps. Not in Switzerland. 5–7.

6 *Buphthalmum speciosissimum* Ard.
Greater Yellow Ox-Eye
Telekia speciosissima (Ard.) Ness

A sturdy plant, with large, oval-acuminate leaves, embracing the stem. Flowers large, deep orange. Local, in the Bergamasque Alps, between L. Como and L. Garda. 6-9.

Buphthalmum salicifolium L.
Yellow Ox-Eye

8–20 ins. Leaves lanceolate to linear-lanceolate, downy. Flowers large, bright yellow and solitary. Widespread, on rocky slopes and in dry meadows, up to over 6000 ft. 6–9.

1

2

3

4

5

6

Plate 96

COMPOSITAE (*continued*)

1 *Hieracium villosum* Jacq.
   Woolly Hawkweed

4–12 ins. Plant without stolons. Stem, leaves and calyx, covered with long white woolly hair. Flowers clear yellow, borne singly, 1–3 per stem, at the tips of the branches. Dry limestone meadows, from about 4800–7800 ft. 7–8

2 *Hieracium aurantiacum* L.
   Orange Hawkweed,
   Devil's Paint Brush

8–16 ins. Plant stoloniferous, sparsely hairy. Flowers reddish-orange to orange-yellow, borne 2–6, in a tight corymb. Local, on non-limy soil. 6–8.

3 *Hieracium intybaceum* All.
   Chicory-leaved Hawkweed

4–12 ins. Leaves yellowish-green, longly lanceolate, with wavy toothed edges. Stem with forked branches, each bearing a single whitish-yellow flower. Rocky non-limy meadows. Local, from 3000–8000 ft. 6–8.

4 *Hieracium echioides* Lumn.
   Hairy Hawkweed

Leaves lanceolate, in ground rosettes. Stems tall, slender, leafless. Flowers yellow in a tightly compact, umbel-like, head. Local, Southern Alps. 7–8.

5 *Hieracium alpicola* Schle.
   Silky-haired Hawkweed

4–8 ins. Leaves spatulate, freely covered with starry hairs. Stem grey-tomentose, with a few small hairy leaves. Flower yellow, with involucre silky haired. Rocky meadows in the Valais, and Savoy. 7–8.

6 *Hieracium pilosella* L.
   Mouse-ear Hawkweed

2–8 ins. Plant stoloniferous, with the leaves on the stolons decreasing in size towards the tip. Leaves hairy above and white-tomentose below. Flowers yellow, occasionally striped purple on the outside, and borne singly, on leafless stems. Common, up to 9000 ft. 5–10.

1

2

3

4

5

6

Glossary of Latin, German and French Names

ACERAS		ACÉRAS
A. anthropophorum	Ohnsporn	A. Hommependu
ACHILLEA	SCHAFGARBE	ACHILLÉE
A. atrata	Schwarzrandige Sch.	A. noirâtre
A. clavenae	Bittere Sch.	A. de Clavena
A. macrophylla	Grossblättrige Sch.	A. à grandes feuilles
A. millefolium	Gemeine Sch.	A. Millefeuille
A. moschata	Moschus Sch.	A. musquée
A. nana	Zwerg Sch.	A. naine
A. oxyloba	Dolomiten Sch.	A. à lobes aigus
A. tomentosa	Filzige Sch.	A. tomenteuse
ACONITUM	EISENHUT	ACONIT
A. anthora	Blassgelber E.	A. Anthora
A. cammarum	Garten E.	A. des jardins
A. lycoctonum	Gelber E.	A. Tue-loup
A. napellus	Blauer E.	A. Napel
A. paniculatum	Rispiger E.	A. paniculé
A. ranunculifolium	Hahnenfussblättriger E.	A. à feuilles de Renoncule
A. variegatum	Gescheckter E.	A. panaché
ACTAEA		
A. spicata	Christophskraut	Herbe de St Christophe
ADENOSTYLES	ALPENDOST	ADENOSTYLE
A. alliariae	Grauer A.	A. à feuilles d'Alliaire
A. glabra	Kahler A.	A. glabre
A. leucophylla	Filziger A.	A. à feuilles blanches
ADONIS	ADONIS	ADONIS
A. flammeus	Feuerroter A.	A. Flamme
A. vernalis	Frühlings-A.	A. du printemps
AJUGA	GUNSEL	BUGLE
A. pyramidalis	Pyramiden G.	B. pyramidale
A. reptans	Kriechender G.	B. rampante
ALCHEMILLA	FRAUENMANTEL	ALCHÉMILLE
A. alpina	Silbermantel	A. des Alpes
A. conjuncta	Verwachsenblättriger F.	A. à feuilles soudées
A. pentaphylla	Fünfblättriger F.	A. à cinq folioles
ALLIUM	LAUCH	AIL
A. insubricum	Insubrischer L.	A. d'Insubrie
A. pulchellum	Schöner L.	A. élégant
A. schoenoprasum	Schnittlauch	Civette
A. sibiricum	Sibirischer-L.	A. de Sibérie
A. victoriale	Allermansharnisch	A. victoriale
AMELANCHIER		
A. ovalis	Felsen mispel	Néflier des rochers
ANACAMPTIS		ANACAMPTIS
A. pyramidalis	Spitzorchis	A. en pyramide
ANCHUSA	OCHSENZUNGE	BUGLOSSE
A. italica	Italienische O.	B. d'Italie
A. officinalis	Gebraüchliche O.	B. officinale
ANDROSACE	MANNSCHILD	ANDROSACE
A. alpina	Alpen M.	A. des Alpes
A. carnea	Roter M.	A. couleur de chair
A. chamaejasme	Bewimperter M.	A. petit jasmin
A. helvetica	Schweizerischer M.	A. de Suisse
A. imbricata	Vandelli's M.	A. de Vandelli

A. lactea	Milchweisser M.	A. couleur de lait
A. obtusifolia	Stumpfblättriger M.	A. à feuilles obtuses
A. pubescens	Weichhaariger M.	A. pubescente
ANEMONE	WINDROSCHEN	ANÉMONE
A. baldensis	Monte Baldo W.	A. du Mt Baldo
A. narcissiflora	Narzissen	A. à fleur de Narcisse
A. nemorosa	Busch W.	A. des bois
A. ranunculoides	Gelbes W.	A. fausse Renoncule
A. trifolia	Dreiblättrige W.	A. à trois feuilles
ANTENNARIA	KATZENFOCHTEN	ANTENNARIA, PIED DE CHAT
A. carpathica	Karpaten K.	A. des Carpathes
A. dioica	Gemeines K.	A. dioïque
ANTHERICUM	GRASLILIE	ANTHERICUM
A. liliago	Astlose G.	A. à fleur de lis
A. ramosum	Astige G.	A. rameux
ANTHYLLIS	WUNDKLEE	ANTHYLLIDE
A. montana	Berg W.	A. des montagnes
A. vulneraria	Gemeiner W.	A. vulnéraire
APHYLLANTHES		APHYLLANTHE
A. monspeliensis	Blauster binse	A. de Montpellier
APOSERIS		APOSERIS
A. foetida	Hainlattich	A. fétide
AQUILEGIA	AKELEI	ANCOLIE
A. alpina	Alpen-akelei	A. des Alpes
A. einseleana	Einseles A.	A. d'Einsele
A. reuteri	Reuters A.	A. de Reuter
A. vulgaris	Gemeine-akelei	A. vulgaire
ARABIS	GANSEKRESSF	ARABETTE
A. alpina	Alpen-gansekresse	A. des Alpes
A. bellidifolia	Masslieb G.	A. à feuilles de Pâquerette
A. coerulea	Bläuliche G.	A. bleuâtre
A. pumila	Zwerg G.	A. naine
ARCTOSTAPHYLOS	BARENTRAUBE	RAISON D'OURS
A. alpina	Alpen B.	R. d'ours des Alpes
A. uva-ursi	Immergrüne B.	R. d'ours commun
ARENARIA	SANDKRAUT	SABLINE
A. biflora	Zweiblütiger S.	S. à deux fleurs
A. ciliata	Bewimpertes S.	S. ciliée
A. grandiflora	Grossblütiges S.	S. à grandes fleurs
ARMERIA	GRASNELKE	STATICE
A. alpina	Alpen G.	S. des Alpes
ARNICA	ARNIKA	ARNICA
A. montana	Wohlverleih	A. des montagnes
ARTEMISIA	EDELRAUTE	ARMOISE
A. genipii	Schwarze E.	A. genipi
A. glacialis	Gletscher E.	A. des glaciers
A. laxa	Echte E.	A. lâche
ARUNCUS		ARONCE
A. sylvestris	Geissbart	A. sauvage, Barbe de bouc, Reine des bois
ASPERULA	WALDMEISTER	ASPÉRULE
A. cynanchica	Hugel-W.	A. à l'esquinancie
ASPHODELUS	AFFODILL	ASPHODÈLE
A. albus	Affodill	A. blanc
ASTER	ASTER	ASTER
A. alpinus	Alpen-A.	A. des Alpes
A. amellus	Berg A.	A. ammelle
ASTRAGALUS	TRAGANT	ASTRAGALE
A. alpinus	Alpen-T.	A. des Alpes
A. australis	Südlicher-T.	A. austral
A. depressus	Niedriger T.	A. naine
A. exscapus	Stengelloser T.	A. sans tige
A. glycyphyllos	Susser T.	A. à feuille de Réglisse
A. leontinus	Tiroler T.	A. de Lienz

A. monspessulanus	Französischer T.	A. de Montpellier
A. onobrychis	Esparsetten T.	A. esparcette
A. sempervirens	Immergrüner T.	A. toujours vert
ASTRANTIA	STERNDOLDE	ASTRANCE
A. major	Grosse S.	Grande A.
A. minor	Kleine S.	Petite A.
ATROPA		ATROPA
A. belladonna	Tollkirsche	A. Belladone
BARTSIA	BARTSCHIE	BARTSIE
B. alpina	Alpen B.	B. des Alpes
BELLIDIASTRUM		
B. michelii	Alpenmasslieb	Fausse Pâquerette
BERBERIS	BERBERITZE	
B. vulgaris	Gemeine B.	Épine-vinette
BISCUTELLA	BRILLENSCHOTCHEN	LUNETIÈRE
B. laevigata	Gemeines Br.	L. lisse
BORAGO	BORETSCH	BOURRACHE
B. officinalis	Boretsch	B. officinale
BUPHTHALMUM		BUPHTHALMUM
B. salicifolium	Rindsauge	B. à feuilles de Saule
B. speciosissimum	Telekie	Telekie remarquable
BUPLEURUM	HASENOHR	BUPLÈVRE
B. longifolium	Langblättriges H.	B. à longues feuilles
B. petraeum	Felsen H.	B. des rochers
B. stellatum	Stern-H.	B. étoilé
CALAMINTHA	KALAMINTHE	CALAMENT
C. alpina	Alpen K.	C. des Alpes
CALLIANTHEMUM	SCHMUCKBLUME	CALLIANTHEMUM
C. coriandrifolium	Schmuckblume	C. à feuilles de Coriandre
C. kerneranum	Kerners S.	C. de Kerner
CALLUNA		FAUSSE BRUYÈRE
C. vulgaris	Bessenheide	Fausse Bruyère
CALTHA		CALTHA
C. palustris	Dotterblume	C. des marais
CAMPANULA	GLOCKENBLUME	CAMPANULE
C. allionii	Alpen G.	C. des Alpes
C. barbata	Bart-G.	C. barbue
C. bononiensis	Bologneser G.	C. de Bologne
C. cenisia	Mont Cenis G.	C. du Mt Cenis
C. cervicaria	Borsten G.	C. cervicaire
C. cochlearifolia	Neidliche G.	C. menue
C. excisa	Ausgeschnittene G.	C. incisée
C. glomerata	Buschel G.	C. agglomérée
C. linifolia	Leinblättrige G.	C. à feuilles de Lin
C. morettiana	Morettis G.	C. de Moretti
C. patula	Lockerrispige G.	C. étalée
C. persicifolia	Pfirsichblättrige G.	C. à feuilles de Pêcher
C. petraea	Veroneser G.	C. des rochers
C. raineri	Insubrische G.	C. de Rainer
C. rapunculoides	Auslaufertribende G.	C. fausse Raiponce
C. rapunculus	Rapunzel G.	C. Raiponce
C. rhomboidalis	Rautenblättrige G.	C. rhomboidale
C. scheuchzeri	Scheuchzers G.	C. de Scheuchzer
C. sibirica	Sibirische G.	C. de Sibérie
C. spicata	Ahren G.	C. en épi
C. thyrsoides	Strauss-G.	C. en thyrse
C. trachelium	Nessel-G.	C. Gantelée
CARDAMINE	SCHAUMKRAUT, ZAHNWURZ	CARDAMINE
C. alpina	Alpen S.	C. des alpes
C. bulbifera	Knollchen-Z.	C. à bulbilles
C. heptaphylla	Fieder-Z.	C. à 7 folioles
C. pentaphyllos	Finger-Z.	C. à 5 folioles

C. polyphylla	Gelbliche-Z.	C. de kitaibel, C. jaunâtre
C. resedifolia	Resedablätt S.	C. à feuilles de Reseda
CARDUUS	DISTEL	CHARDON
C. defloratus	Felsen-D.	C. décapité
C. nutans	Nickende-D.	C. penché
C. personatus	Gebirgs-D.	C. Bardane
CARLINA	EBERWURZ	CARLINE
C. acanthifolia	Akanthus blättrige E.	C. à feuilles d'Acanthe
C. acaulis	Stengellose E.	C. sans tige
CENTAUREA	FLOCKENBLUME	CENTAURÉE
C. cyanus	Kornblume	Bluet
C. montana	Berg-F.	C. des montagnes
C. nervosa	Federige F.	C. nervée
C. rhapontica	Riesen-F.	C. Rhapontic
C. scabiosa	Skabiosen-F.	C. scabieuse
C. uniflora	Einblütige-F.	C. à une fleur
CENTRANTHUS	SPORNBLUME	CENTRANTHE
C. angustifolius	Schmalblättrige S.	C. à feuilles étroites
C. ruber	Rote S.	C. rouge
CEPHALANTHERA	WALDVOGELEIN	CEPHALANTHÈRE
C. alba	Weissliches W.	C. blanchâtre
C. longifolia	Langblättriges W.	C. à longues feuilles
C. rubra	Rotes-W.	C. rouge
CEPHALARIA	KOPFBLUME	CEPHALAIRE
C. alpina	Alpen-K.	C. des Alpes
CERASTIUM	HORNKRAUT	CERAISTE
C. arvense ssp. strictum	Acker-H.	C. des champs
C. latifolium	Breitblättriges H.	C. à larges feuilles
C. uniflorum	Einblütiges H.	C. uniflore
CERINTHE	WACHSBLUME	MELINET
C. glabra	Alpen-W.	M. glabre
CHAMORCHIS	ZWERGORCHIS	CHAMORCHIS
C. alpina	Zwergorchis	C. des Alpes
CHEIRANTHUS	GOLDLACK	GIROFLÉE
C. cheiri	Goldlack	G. jaune
CHRYSANTHEMUM	WUCHTERBLUME	CHRYSANTHÈME
C. alpinum	Alpen-W.	Ch. des Alpes
C. leucanthemum	Wiesen-W.	Grande Marguerite
CHRYSOSPLENIUM	MILZKRAUT	DORINE
C. alternifolium	Wechselblättriges M.	D. à feuilles alternes
C. oppositifolium	Gegenblättriges M.	D. à feuilles opposées
CICERBITA	MILCHLATTICH	CICERBITE
C. alpina	Alpen-M.	C. des Alpes
CIRSIUM	KRATZDISTEL	CIRSE
C. acaulon	Stengellose K.	C. sans tige
C. eristhales	Klebrige K.	C. glutineux
C. eriophorum	Wollkopfige K.	C. Laineux
C. heterophyllum	Verschiedenblättriges K.	C. Fausse Hélénie
C. oleraceum	Kohl-Distel	C. maraîcher
C. spinosissimum	Alpen-K.	C. épineux
CISTUS	ZISTROSE	CISTE
C. albidus	Rote Z.	C. cotonneux
C. salvifolius	Salbeiblättriges Z.	C. à feuilles de Sauge
CLEMATIS	ALPENREBE	CLÉMATITE
C. alpina	Alpenrebe	C. des Alpes
COELOGLOSSUM		COELOGLOSSUM
C. viride	Hart-Orchis	C. verdâtre
COLCHICUM	ZEITLOSE	COLCHIQUE
C. alpinum	Alpen-Z.	C. des Alpes
C. autumnale	Herbst-Z.	C. d'automne
COLUTEA	BLASENSTRAUCH	BAGUENAUDIER
C. arborescens	Gemeine B.	B. arborescent
CONVALLARIA	MAIGLÖCKCHEN	MUGUET
C. majalis	Maiglöckchen	M. de Mai

CORALLORHIZA	KORALLENWURZ	CORALLORHIZA
C. trifida	Korallenwurz	C. trifide
CORONILLA	KRONWICKE	CORONILLE
C. coronata	Berg K.	C. en couronne, C. des montagnes
C. emerus	Strauchwicke	C. Emerus
C. varia	Bunte K.	C. bigarrée
CORYDALIS	LERCHENSPORN	CORYDALE
C. lutea	Gelber L.	C. jaune
CREPIS	PIPPAU	CRÉPIDE
C. aurea	Orangeroter P.	C. orangée
CROCUS	SAFRAN	SAFRAN
C. albiflorus	Frühlings S.	S. à fleurs blanches
CYCLAMEN	ALPENVEILCHEN	CYCLAMEN
C. europaeum	Gewöhnliches A.	C. d'Europe
C. neapolitanum	Neapolitanisches A.	C. de Naples
CYPRIPEDIUM		
C. calceolus	Frauenschuh	Sabot de Vénus
CYTISUS	GEISSKLEE	CYTISE
C. decumbens	Liegender G.	C. rampant
C. emeriflorus	Strauchwicker G.	C. à fleurs de Coronille Emerus
C. hirsutus	Rauchhaariger G.	C. hérissé
C. nigricans	Schwarzwerdender G.	C. noirissant
C. radiatus	Strahliger G.	C. rayonnant
C. sagittalis	Geflügelter G.	C. sagitte
C. sessilifolius	Blattstieloser G.	C. à feuilles sessiles
DAPHNE	SEIDELBAST	DAPHNE
D. alpina	Alpen-S.	D. des Alpes
D. cneorum	Fluhroschen	D. Camelée
D. mezereum	Gemeiner S.	D. bois gentil
D. petraea	Berg-S.	D. des rochers
D. striata	Steinroschen	D. strié
DELPHINIUM	RITTERSPORN	DAUPHINELLE
D. consolida	Feld R.	Pied d'alouette
D. elatum	Hoher R.	D. élevée
DIANTHUS	NELKE	ŒILLET
D. alpinus	Alpen-N.	Œ. des Alpes
D. barbatus	Bart-N.	Œ. barbue
D. carthusianorum	Karthäuser N.	Œ. de Chartreux
D. caryophyllus ssp. sylvestris	Wald-N.	Œ. des bois
D. glacialis	Gletscher N.	Œ. des glaciers
D. gratianopolitanus	Grenobler N.	Œ. bleuâtre
D. hyssopifolius	Ysop-N.	Œ. à feuilles d'Hysope
D. neglectus	Ubersehene N.	Œ. négligé
D. seguieri	Seguiers N.	Œ. de Seguier
D. superbus	Pracht-N.	Œ. superbe
DICTAMNUS	DIPTAM	FRAXINELLE
D. albus	Diptam	Fraxinelle
DIGITALIS	FINGERHUT	DIGITALE
D. grandiflora	Blassgelber F.	D. à grandes fleurs
D. lutea	Gelber-F.	D. jaune
DORONICUM	GEMSWURZ	DORONIC
D. clusii	Clusius' G.	D. de Clusius
D. cordatum	Herzblättrige G.	D. à feuilles en cœur
D. grandiflorum	Grosskopfige G.	D. à grandes fleurs
DOUGLASIA	GOLDPRIMEL	DOUGLASIE
D. vitaliana	Goldprimel	Douglasie
DRABA	FELSENBLUMCHEN	DRAVE
D. aizoides	Immergrünes F.	D. Faux Aizoon
D. dubia	Gletscher F.	D. douteuse
D. tomentosa	Filziges F.	D. tomenteuse
DRACOCEPHALUM	DRACHENKOPF	TÊTE DE DRAGON
D. austriacum	Österreichischer D.	Tête de Dr. d'Autriche
D. ruyschianum	Berg-D.	Tête de Dr. de Ruysch

DRYAS
D. octopetala — Silberwurz — **DRYADE** D. à 7 pétales

ECHIUM
E. vulgare — **NATTERKOPF** Gemeines N. — **VIPERINE** V. vulgaire

EMPETRUM
E. nigrum — Krahenbeere — **CAMARINE** C. noire

EPILOBIUM
E. angustifolium — **WEIDENROSCHEN** Wald-W. — **EPILOBE** E. à feuilles étroites
E. dodonaei — Rosmarin W. — E. Rosmarin
E. fleischeri — Fleischers W. — E. de Fleischer

EPIPACTIS
E. atropurpurea — **SUMPFWURZ** Braunerote S. — **EPIPACTIS** E. pourpre-noirâtre
E. latifolia — Breitblättrige S. — E. à larges feuilles
E. microphylla — Kleinblättrige S. — E. à petites feuilles
E. palustris — Gemeine S. — E. des marais
E. purpurata — Violettrote S. — E. pourprée

EPIPOGIUM
E. aphyllum — Ohnblatt — **EPIPOGIUM** E. sans feuilles

ERICA
E. carnea — Schneeheide — **BRUYÈRE** B. couleur de chair

ERIGERON
E. alpinus — **BERUFKRAUT** Alpen-B. — **ERIGERON** E. des Alpes
E. uniflorus — Einkopfiger B. — E. à une tête

ERINUS
E. alpinus — Leberbalsam — **ERINE** E. des Alpes

ERITRICHIUM
E. nanum — Himmelsherold — Roi des Alpes

ERYNGIUM
E. alpinum — **MANNSTREU** Alpen-M. — **CHARDON BLEU** C. bl. alpin

ERYSIMUM
E. helveticum — **SCHOTERICH** Schweizerischer Sch. — **VELAR** V. de Suisse

EUPHORBIA
E. cyparissias — **WOLFSMILCH** Zypressen W. — **EUPHORBE** E. faux Cyprès

EUPHRASIA
E. minima — **AUGENTROST** Kleiner A. — **EUPHRAISE** E. naine

FRAGARIA
F. vesca — **ERDBEERE** Wald-E. — **FRAISE** F. des bois

FRITILLARIA
F. involucrata — **SCHACHBLUME** Stengelblättriges S. — **FRITILLAIRE** F. involucre
F. meleagris — Schachblume — F. Pintade-Damier

GAGEA
G. fistulosa — **GELBSTERN** Rohriger G. — **GAGÉE** G. jaune

GALIUM
G. helveticum — **LABKRAUT** Schweizerischer L. — **GAILLET** G. de Suisse
G. pumilum — Rauhes L. — G. naine

GENISTA
G. pilosa — **GINSTER** Behaarter-G. — **GENÊT** G. poilu
G. tinctoria — Ferber-G. — G. des teinturiers

GENTIANA
G. alpina — **ENZIAN** Alpen E. — **GENTIANE** G. des Alpes
G. angustifolia — Schmalblättriger E. — G. à feuilles étroites
G. asclepiadea — Schwalbenwurz E. — G. à feuilles d'Asclépiade
G. bavarica — Bayerischer E. — G. de Bavère
G. brachyphylla — Kurzblättriger E. — G. à feuilles courtes
G. ciliata — Gefranstor E. — G. cilée
G. clusii — Clusius' E. — G. de Clusius
G. cruciata — Kreuz-E. — G. Croisette
G. germanica — Deutscher E. — G. d'Allemagne
G. imbricata — — G. imbriquée
G. kochiana — Kochs E. — G. de Koch
G. lutea — Gelber E. — G. jaune

G. nivalis	Schnee E.	G. des neiges
G. orbicularis	Rundblättriges E.	G. à feuilles orbiculaires
G. pannonica	Ostalpen E.	G. de Hongrie
G. pneumonanthe	Lungen E.	G. des marais
G. punctata	Getüpfelter E.	G. ponctuée
G. purpurea	Purpur E.	G. pourprée
G. tenella	Zarter E.	G. délicate
G. utriculosa	Schlauch E.	G. à calice renflé
G. verna	Frühlings E.	G. printanière
GENTIANELLA	ENZIAN	GENTIANE
G. campestris	Feld-E.	G. champêtre
GERANIUM	STORCHSCHNABEL	GERANIUM
G. argenteum ssp. cinereum	Silber S.	G. argenté
G. nodosum	Knotige S.	G. noueux
G. palustre	Sumpf S.	G. des marais
G. phaeum	Brauner S.	
var. lividum	Trubvioletter S.	G. livide
G. rivulare	Weisser S.	G. blanc
G. sanguineum	Blutroter S.	G. rouge sang
G. sylvaticum	Wald S.	G. des bois
GEUM	BERGNELKENWURZ	SIEVERSIE
G. montanum	Gemeine B.	S. des montagnes
G. reptans	Kriechende B.	S. rampante
G. rivale	Bach Nelkenwurz	Benoîte des ruisseaux
GLADIOLUS	GLADIOLE – SIEGWURZ	GLAÏEUL
G. palustris	Sumpf-G.	G. des marais
G. segetum	Saat-G.	G. des moissons
GLOBULARIA	KUGELBLUME	GLOBULAIRE
G. cordifolia	Herzblättrige K.	G. à feuilles en cœur
G. elongata	Gemeine K.	G. vulgaire
G. nudicaulis	Schaft K.	G. à tige nue
GNAPHALIUM	RUHRKRAUT	GNAPHALE
G. hoppeanum	Hoppes R.	G. de Hoppe
G. supinum	Niedriges R.	G. couche
G. sylvaticum	Wald R.	G. des bois
GOODYERA		GOODYÈRE
G. repens	Moosorchid	G. rampante
GYMNADENIA	HANDWURZ	GYMNADENIA
G. conopsea	Langspornige H.	G. Moucheron
G. odoratissima	Wohlreichende H.	G. odorant
GYPSOPHILA	GIPSKRAUT	GYPSOPHILE
G. repens	Kriechendes G.	G. rampante
HEDYSARUM		HEDYSARUM
H. obscurum	Sussklee	H. des Alpes
HÉLIANTHEMUM	SONNENROSCHEN	HÉLIANTHÈME
H. alpestre	Alpen S.	H. alpestre
H. apenninum	Apenninen S.	H. des Apennins
H. canum	Graufilziger S.	H. blanchâtres
H. nummularium	Gemeines S.	H. commun
HELLEBORUS	NIESWURZ	ELLEBORE
H. foetidus	Stinkende N.	E. fétide
H. viridis	Grune N.	E. vert
HEPATICA	LEBERBLUMCHEN	HÉPATIQUE
H. nobilis		H. à 3 lobes
HERMINIUM		HERMINIUM
H. monorchis	Einorchis	H. à un bulbe
HIERACIUM	HABICHTSKRAUT	ÉPERVIÈRE
H. alpicola	Seidenhaariges H.	E. alpicole
H. aurantiacum	Orangeroten H.	E. orangée
H. echioides	Natterkopfige H.	E. à feuilles de Viperine
H. intybaceum	Weissliches H.	E. à feuilles de Chicorée
H. pilosella	Langhaariges H.	E. pilosella
H. villosum	Zottiges H.	E. velue

HIPPOCREPIS	HUFEISENKLEE	HIPPOCRÉPIDE
H. comosa	Hufeisenklee	H. à toupet
HOMOGYNE		HOMOGYNE
H. alpina	Alpenlattich	H. des Alpes
HORMINUM		HORMIN
H. pyrenaicum	Drachenmaul	H. des Pyrénées
HUTCHINSIA		HUTCHINSIE
H. alpina	Gemskresse	H. des Alpes
HYPOCHOERIS	FERKELKRAUT	
H. uniflora	Einkopfige F.	Porcelle à une tête
IBERIS	BAUERN SENF	IBERIS
I. saxatilis	Felsen-B. S.	I. des rochers
ISATIS		
I. tinctoria	Waid	Pastel des teinturiers
JASIONE	JASIONE	JASIONE
J. montana	Berg-J.	J. des montagnes
KNAUTIA	WITWENBLUME	KNAUTIE
K. sylvatica	Wald-W.	K. des bois
LACTUCA	LATTICH	LAITUE
L. perennis	Blauer L.	L. vivace
LASERPITUM	LASERKRAUT	LASER
L. latifolium	Breitblättriges L.	L. à larges feuilles
L. siler	Berg-L.	Sermontain
LATHYRUS	PLATTERBSE	GESSE
L. latifolius	Breitblättrige Pl.	G. à larges feuilles
L. levigatus	Gelbe Pl.	G. jaune
L. montanus	Berg Pl.	G. des montagnes
L. pratensis	Wiesen Pl.	G. des prés
L. niger	Schwarze Pl.	G. noire
L. sylvestris	Wald Pl.	G. des bois
L. tuberosus	Knollige Pl.	G. tubereuse
L. vernus	Frühlings Pl.	G. printanière
LEONTOPODIUM		
L. alpinum	Edelweiss	Étoile des Alpes
LEPIDIUM		
L. draba	Pfeil-Kresse	Passerage Drave
LEUCOJUM	KNOTENBLUME	
L. vernum	Frühlings-K.	Nivéole du Printemps
LEUCORCHIS	HANDWURZ	GYMNADENIA
L. albida	Weissliche H.	G. blanchâtre
LIGUSTICUM	LIEBSTOCK	LIGUSTIQUE
L. mutellina	Alpen-L.	L. mutelline
L. mutellinoides	Kleiner L.	L. Fausse Mutelline
LILIUM	LILIE	LIS
L. martagon	Turkenbund	L. Martagon
L. bulbiferum	Feuerlilie	L. orangé
ssp. croceum	Feuerlilie	L. orangé
LIMODORUM		LIMODORUM
L. abortivum	Dingel	L. à feuilles avortées
LINARIA	LEINKRAUT	LINAIRE
L. alpina	Alpen-L.	L. des Alpes
LINNAEA		LINNÉE
L. borealis	Moosglockchen	L. boréale
LINUM	LEIN	LIN
L. alpinum	Alpen-L.	L. des Alpes
L. tenuifolium	Feinblättriger-L.	L. à feuilles menues
L. viscosum	Klebriger L.	L. visqueuse
LISTERA	ZWEIBLATT	LISTERA
L. cordata	Moor-Z.	L. en cœur

L. ovata	Weisen-Z.	L. ovale
LITHOSPERMUM	**STEINSAME**	**GREMIL**
L. purpureo-coeruleum	Blauer S.	G. rouge-bleu
LLOYDIA	**FALTENLILIE**	**LOIDIE**
L. serotina	Faltenlilie	L. tardive
LOISELEURIA	**ALPENAZALEE**	**LOISELEURIE**
L. procumbens	Alpenazalee	L. couchée
LONICERA	**GEISSBLATT**	**LONICERA**
L. alpigena	Alpen G.	L. des alpes
L. coerulea	Blaues G.	L. bleu
L. nigra	Schwarzes G.	L. noir
L. xylosteum	Rotes G.	L. des haies
LOROGLOSSUM		**HIMANTOGLOSSE**
L. hircinum	Riemenzunge	H. à odeur de bouc
LOTUS	**SCHOTENKLEE**	**LOTIER**
L. corniculatus	Wiesen S.	L. corniculé
L. pedunculatus	Sumpf-S.	L. des marais
LUNARIA		**LUNAIRE**
L. annua	Silberling	Monnaie du Pape
L. rediviva	Wilde-Mondviole	L. vivace
LYCHNIS		**LYCHNIS**
L. alpina	Alpen-Pechnelke	L. des Alpes
L. flos-cuculi	Kuckucks-Lichtnelke	L. Fleur de coucou
L. flos-jovis	Jupiternelke	L. Fleur de Jupiter
L. viscaria	Gemeine-Pechnelke	L. vulgaire
MAIANTHEMUM		
M. bifolium	Schattenblume	Petit Muguet
MATTHIOLA		
M. fruticulosa ssp. valesiaca	Walliser leukoje	Violier du Valais
MELAMPYRUM	**WACHTELWIEZEN**	**MELAMPYRE**
M. nemorosum	Hain W.	M. des bois
M. pratense	Wiesen W.	M. des prés
M. silvaticum	Wald W.	M. des forêts
MELILOTUS	**HONIGKLEE**	**MELILOT**
M. albus	Weisser H.	M. blanc
M. altissimus	Hoher H.	M. élevé
M. officinalis	Gebräuchlicher H.	M. officinal
MELITTIS		**MELITTE**
M. melissophyllum	Immenblatt	M. à feuilles de Mélisse
MENTHA	**MINZE**	**MENTHE**
M. longifolia	Ross-M.	M. à longues feuilles
MEUM		
M. athamanthicum	Barenwurz	Fenouil des Alpes
MINUARTIA	**MIERE**	**MINUARTIE**
M. biflora	Zweiblütige M.	M. à deux fleurs
M. capillacea	Feinblättrige M.	M. à feuilles capillaires
M. laricifolia	Nadelblättrige M.	M. à feuilles de Mélèze
M. recurva	Krummblättrige M.	M. recourbée
M. sedoides	Zwerg-M.	M. faux-Sedum
M. verna	Frühlings-M.	M. du Printemps
M. villarsii	Villars M.	M. de Villars
MOEHRINGIA	**NABELMIERE**	**MOEHRINGIE**
M. ciliata	Bewimperte N.	M. ciliée
M. muscosa	Moos-N.	M. Mousse
MOLOPOSPERMUM		**MOLOPOSPERME**
M. peloponesiacum	Striemensame	M. de Péloponèse
MONESES	**WINTERGRUN**	**PIROLE**
M. uniflora	Einblütiges W.	P. à une fleur
MONOTROPA		**MONOTROPE**
M. hypopitys	Fichtenspargel	M. Sucepin
MUSCARI	**BISAMHYAZINTHE**	**MUSCARI**
M. comosum	Schopfartige B.	M. à Louppe
M. racemosum	Weinsbergs B.	M. à fleurs en grappe

MYOSOTIS		**MYOSOTIS**
M. alpestris	Alpen-Vergissmeinnicht	M. alpestre
NARCISSUS	**NARZISSE**	**NARCISSE**
N. exsertus	Berg-N.	N. à feuilles étroites
N. pseudo-narcissus	Gelbe-N.	N. jaune
NEOTTIA		**NÉOTTIE**
N. nidus-avis	Nestwurz	N. Nid d'oiseau
NIGRITELLA	**MANNERTREU**	**NIGRITELLE**
N. nigra	Schwarz M.	Orchis vanille
N. rubra	Rote-M.	N. rouge
ONOBRYCHIS	**ESPARSETTE**	**ESPARCETTE**
O. viciifolia	Saat-E.	Sainfoin, E. à feuilles de vesce
var. montana	Berg-E.	E. des montagnes
ONONIS	**HAUHECHEL**	**BUGRANE**
O. natrix	Gelbes-H.	Ononis jaune
O. repens	Kreichende H.	B. naine
O. rotundifolia	Rundblättrige H.	Ononis à feuilles rondes
O. spinosa	Dornige-H.	Arrête-bœuf
OPHRYS		**OPHRYS**
O. apifera	Bienenblume	O. abeille
O. aranifera	Spinnenblume	O. araignée
O. fuciflora	Hummelblume	O. bourdon
O. muscifera	Fliegenblume	O. mouche
ORCHIS	**ORCHIS**	**ORCHIS**
O. coriophora	Wanzen-O.	O. punaise
O. globosa	Kugel-O.	O. globuleux
O. incarnata	Fleischrote O.	O. incarnat
O. latifolia	Breitblättrige O.	O. à larges feuilles
O. laxiflora	Lockerblütige O.	O. à fleurs lâches
O. maculata	Gefleckte O.	O. tacheté
O. mascula	Stattliche O.	O. mâle
O. militaris	Helm-O.	O. militaire
O. morio	Kleine O.	O. Bouffon
O. pallens	Blasse O.	O. pâle
O. palustris	Sumpf O.	O. des marais
O. papilionacea	Schmetterling	O. papillon
O. provincialis	Provenzalische O.	O. de Provence
O. purpurea	Braunrote O.	O. pourpré
O. sambucina	Holunder O.	O. à odeur de Sureau
O. simia	Affen O.	O. singe
O. traunsteineri	Traunsteiners O.	O. de Traunsteiner
O. tridentata	Dreizähniges O.	O. dentelé
O. ustulata	Schwarzkopfige O.	O. brûlé
ORIGANUM		**ORIGAN**
O. vulgare	Dost	O. vulgaire
ORLAYA		**ORLAYA**
O. grandiflora	Breitsame	O. à grandes fleurs
ORTHILIA	**WINTERGRUN**	**PIROLE**
O. secunda	Einseitwendiges W.	P. unilaterale
ORNITHOGALUM	**MILCHSTERN**	**ORNITHOGALE**
O. pyrenaicum	Pyrenaen M.	Aspergette
O. umbellatum	Doldiger M.	Dame d'onze heures
OROBANCHE	**SOMMERWURZ**	**OROBANCHE**
O. hederae	Efeu S.	O. du Lierre
OXALIS	**SAUERKLEE**	
O. acetosella	Gemeiner-S.	Pain Coucou
OXYRIA		**OXYRIA**
O. digyna	Sauerling	O. à deux styles
OXYTROPIS	**SPITZKIEL**	**OXYTROPIS**
O. campestris	Alpen-S.	O. des Alpes
O. foetida	Drüsiger S.	O. fétide
O. halleri	Hallers S.	O. soyeux

O. lapponica	Lapplander S.	O. de Lapponie
O. montana	Berg-S.	O. des montagnes
O. pilosa	Zottiger S.	O. poilu
O. sericea	Hallers S.	O. de Haller

PAEONIA	PFINGSTROSE	PIVOINE
P. officinalis	Pfingstrose	P. officinale
PAPAVER	MOHN	PAVOT
P. alpinum	Weisser Alpen-M.	P. des Alpes
P. kerneri	Kerners M.	P. de Kerner
P. pyrenaicum ssp. rhaeticum	Gelber Alpen-M.	P. jaune
PARADISIA		PARADISIE
P. liliastrum	Trichterlilie	P. Faux Lis
PARIS		PARISETTE
P. quadrifolia	Einbeere	P. à 4 feuilles
PARNASSIA		PARNASSIE
P. palustris	Studentenroschen	P. des marais
PEDICULARIS	LAUSEKRAUT	PEDICULAIRE
P. asplenifolia	Farnblatt-L.	P. à feuilles d'Asplenium
P. cenisia	Mont Cenis L.	P. du Mt Cenis
P. comosa	Schopfiges L.	P. chevelue
P. elongata	Langähriges S.	
P. foliosa	Blattreiches L.	P. feuillée
P. gyroflexa	Bogenblütiges L.	P. arquée
P. kerneri	Kerners L.	P. de Kerner
P. oederi	Buntes L.	P. de Oeder
P. palustris	Sumpf-L.	P. des marais
P. recucita	Trubrotes L.	P. tronquée
P. rosea	Rosenrotes L.	P. rose
P. rostrato-capitata	Kopfiges L.	P. à bec et en tête
P. rostrato-spicata	Hellrotes L.	P. à bec et en épi
P. sylvatica	Wald-L.	P. des bois
P. tuberosa	Knolliges L.	P. tubereuse
P. verticillata	Quirliges L.	P. verticillée
PETASITES	PESTWURZ	PÉTASITE
P. albus	Weisse P.	P. blanc
P. paradoxus	Alpen P.	P. blanc de neige
PETROCALLIS		PETROCALLIS
P. pyrenaica	Steinschmuckel	P. des Pyrénées
PETRORHAGIA		TUNIQUE
P. nanteuilii	Sprossende Felsennelke	T. prolifère
PHACA	LINSE	PHAQUE
P. alpina	Alpenlinse	P. des Alpes
P. frigida	Gletscherlinse	P. des glaciers
PHYTEUMA	RAPUNZEL	RAIPONCE
P. carestiae	Ratische-R.	R. à feuilles d'Edréanthe
P. comosum	Schopf-R.	R. chevelue
P. globularifolium	Armblütige R.	R. à feuilles de Globulaire
P. hemisphericum	Halbkugelige R.	R. hemisphérique
P. michelii ssp. betonicifolium	Betonika-R.	R. à feuilles de Bétoine
P. orbiculare	Rundkopfige R.	R. orbiculaire
P. ovatum	Hallers R.	R. de Haller
P. scheuchzeri	Scheuchzers R.	R. de Scheuchzer
PINGUICULA	FELTBLATT	GRASSETTE
P. alpina	Alpen-F.	G. des Alpes
P. vulgaris	Gemeines-F.	G. commun
PLATANTHERA	BREITKOLBCHEN	PLATANTHÈRE
P. bifolia	Zweiblättriges B.	P. à deux fleurs
P. chlorantha	Gumliches-B.	P. à fleurs verdâtres
POLEMONIUM		POLÉMONIE
P. coeruleum	Sperrkraut	P. bleu
POLYGALA	KREUZBLUME	POLYGALA
P. alpestris	Berg K.	P. alpestre
P. alpina	Alpen-K.	P. des Alpes

P. chamaebuxus	Buchs-K.	P. Petit Buis
P. vulgaris	Gemeine-K.	P. vulgaire
POLYGONATUM	WEISS-WURZ	POLYGONATE
P. officinale	Salomons-siegel	P. Sceau de Solomon
P. multiflorum	Vielblütige W.	P. multiflore
P. verticillatum	Quirlblättrige W.	P. verticillé
POLYGONUM	KNOTERICH	RENOUÉE
P. bistorta	Schlangen K.	R. Bistorte
P. viviparum	Knollchen K.	R. vivipare
POTENTILLA	FINGERKRAUT	POTENTILLE
P. aurea	Gold-F.	P. dorée
P. caulescens	Stengel-F.	P. caulescente
P. crantzii	Crantz' F.	P. de Crantz
P. nitida	Glanzendes F.	P. luisante
P. rupestris	Felsen-F.	P. des rochers
PRENANTHES		PRENANTHE
P. purpurea	Hasenlattich	P. pourpré
PRIMULA	PRIMEL	PRIMEVÈRE
P. allionii	Allionis P.	P. d'Allioni
P. auricula	Aurikel P.	P. auricule
P. × berninae	Bernina P.	P. de la Bernine
P. daonensis	Sudtiroler P.	P. du Val Daone
P. elatior	Wald-P.	P. élevée
P. farinosa	Mehl-P.	P. farineuse
P. glutinosa	Klebrige P.	P. glutineuse
P. hirsuta	Behaarte P.	P. hérissé
P. integrifolia	Ganzblättrige P.	P. à feuilles entières
P. longiflora	Hallers P.	P. de Haller
P. marginata	Weissrandige P.	P. marginée
P. minima	Swerg-P.	P. naine
P. pedemontana	Piemonteser P.	P. du Piémont
P. spectabilis	Prächtige P.	P. spectaculaire
ssp. clusiana	Clusius' P.	P. de Clusius
ssp. glaucescens	Meergrune-P.	P. glaucescente
P. tirolensis	Tiroler P.	
P. viscosa	Breitblättrige P.	P. visqueuse
PRUNELLA	BRUNELLE	BRUNELLE
P. grandifolia	Grossblutige B.	B. à grandes fleurs
PULMONARIA	LUNGENKRAUT	PULMONAIRE
P. angustifolia	Glaues-L.	P. à feuilles étroites
P. officinalis	Gemeines L.	P. officinale
PULSATILLA	KUCHENSCHELLE	PULSATILLE
P. alpina	Alpen Anemone	P. des Alpes
P. halleri	Hallers K.	P. de Haller
P. montana	Berg K.	P. des montagnes
P. sulphurea	Gelber K.	P. jaune
P. vernalis	Frühlings K.	P. du Printemps
P. vulgaris	Gewöhnliche K.	P. vulgaire, Coquelourde
PYROLA	WINTERGRUN	PIROLE
P. chlorantha	Grunliches W.	P. verdâtre
P. media	Mittleres W.	P. intermédiaire
P. minor	Kleines-W.	Petit P.
P. rotundifolia	Rundblättriges W.	P. à feuilles rondes
RANUNCULUS	HAHNENFUSS	RENONCULE
R. aconitifolius	Eisenhutblättrige H.	R. à feuilles d'Aconit
R. alpestris	Alpen H.	R. alpestre
R. hybridus	Bastard H.	R. hybride
R. montanus	Berg H.	R. des montagnes
R. parnassifolius	Herzblatt H.	R. à feuilles de Parnassie
R. platanifolius	Platanenblättrige H.	R. à feuilles de Platane
R. pyrenaeus	Pyrenaen H.	R. des Pyrénées
R. seguieri	Seguiers H.	R. de Sèguier
R. thora	Schildblättriger H.	R. vénéneuse

RHAMNUS	KREUZDORN	NERPRUN
R. pumila	Zwerg-K.	N. Nain
RHINANTHUS	KLAPPERTOPF	RHINANTHE
R. alectorolophus	Zottiger K.	R. velue
R. angustifolius	Schmalblättriger K.	R. à feuilles étroites
ssp. subalpinus	Voralpen K.	R. des Préalpes
RHODODENDRON	ALPENROSE	RHODODENDRON
R. ferrugineum	Rostblättrige A.	R. ferrugineux
R. hirsutum	Bewimperte A.	R. hérissé
RHODOTHAMNUS		RHODOTHAMNE
R. chamaecistus	Zwerg-Alpenrose	R. Ciste nain
RIBES		GROSEILLER
R. alpinum	Stachelbeere	G. des Alpes
ROSA	HAGROSE	ROSIER
R. pendulina	Alpen-Hagrose	R. des Alpes
RUBUS	BROMBEERE	RONCE
R. saxatilis	Steinbeere	R. des rochers
RUMEX	AMPFER	RUMEX
R. nivalis	Schnee-A.	R. des neiges
R. scutatus	Schild-A.	R. à écussons
SALVIA	SALBEI	SAUGE
S. glutinosa	Klebrige S.	S. glutineuse
S. pratensis	Wiesen-S.	S. des prés
SAMBUCUS	HOLUNDER	SUREAU
S. ebulus	Zwerg-H.	S. Yèble
SAPONARIA	SEIFENKRAUT	SAPONAIRE
S. lutea	Gelbes S.	S. jaune
S. ocymoides	Rotes-S.	S. rose
S. officinalis	Gebrauchliches S.	Savonnière
S. pumilio	Niedriges S.	S. nain
SAUSSUREA	ALPENSCHARTE	SAUSSURÉE
S. alpina	Spinwebartige A.	S. des Alpes
S. discolor	Weissfilzige A.	S. feuilles discolores
SAXIFRAGA	STEINBRECK	SAXIFRAGE
S. aizoides	Bewimperter S.	S. Faux Aizoon
S. aizoon	Trauben-S.	S. Aizoon
S. androsacea	Mannschild S.	S. Androsace
S. aspera	Rauher-S.	S. rude
ssp. bryoides	Moos-S.	S. mousse
S. biflora	Zweiblütiger S.	S. à deux fleurs
S. caesia	Blaulicher S.	S. bleuâtre
S. cotyledon	Strauss S.	S. cotylédon
S. cuneifolia	Kielblättriger S.	S. à feuilles en coin
S. exarata	Gefurchter S.	S. sillonnée
S. hostii	Hosts S.	S. de Host
S. moschata	Moschus S.	S. musquée
S. muscoides	Flachblättriger S.	S. à feuilles planes
S. mutata	Safrangelber S.	S. changée
S. oppositifolia	Gegenblättriger S.	S. à feuilles opposées
S. retusa	Gestutztens S.	S. tronquée
S. rotundifolia	Rundblättriger S.	S. à feuilles rondes
S. seguieri	Seguiers S.	S. de Séguier
S. stellaris	Stern S.	S. étoilée
SCABIOSA	SKABIOSE	SCABIEUSE
S. lucida	Glanzende S.	S. luisant
SCILLA	MEERZWIEBEL	SCILLE
S. bifolia	Zweiblättrige M.	S. à deux feuilles
S. italica	Italienische M.	S. d'Italie
SCORZONERA	SCHWARZWURZEL	SCORSONÈRE
S. aristata	Grannen S.	S. à arêtes
S. purpurea ssp. rosea	Rosanrote S.	S. rose
SCUTELLARIA	HELMKRAUT	SCUTELLAIRE
S. alpina	Alpen-H.	S. des Alpes

SEDUM	MAUERPFEFFER	SEDUM
S. acre	Scharfer M.	S. acre
S. album	Weissen M.	S. blanc
S. alpestre	Alpen M.	S. des Alpes
S. atratum	Dunkler M.	S. noirâtre
S. rupestre	Felsen M.	S. des rochers
S. telephium	Breitblättriges Fettkraut	Reprise
SEMPERVIVUM	HAUSWURZ	JOUBARBE
S. alpinum	Alpen-H.	J. des Alpes
S. arachnoideum	Spinwebartige H.	J. aranéuse
S. montanum	Berg-H.	J. des montagnes
S. tectorum	Eckte H.	J. des toits
S. wulfenii	Wulfens H.	J. de Wulfen
SENECIO	KREUZKRAUT	SENECON
S. alpinus	Alpen K.	S. des Alpes
S. abrotanifolius	Eberreis K.	S. à feuilles d'Auronne
S. doronicum	Gemswurz K.	S. doronic
S. fuchsii	Fuchs K.	S. de Fuchs
S. incanus	Graues-K.	S. blanchâtre
ssp. carniolicus	Krainer K.	S. de la Carniole
S. uniflorus	Einkopfiges K.	S. à un capitule
SERAPIAS		SERAPIAS
S. vomeracea	Stendelwurz	S. à longs pétales
SERRATULA	SCHARTE	SERRATULE
S. tinctoria	Farber-S.	S. des teinturiers
SIEVERSIA	BERGNELKENWURZ	SIEVERSIE
S. reptans	Kreichende B.	S. rampante
S. montana	Gemeine G.	S. des montagnes
SILENE	LEIMKRAUT	SILENE
S. acaulis	Stengelloses L.	S. acaule
ssp. exscapa	Polster-L.	S. sans tige
S. dioica	Rote Waldnelke	Mélandrie rouge
S. elizabethae	Südalpine Waldnelke	Mélandrie d'Elisabeth
S. nutans	Nickendes L.	S. penché
S. rupestris	Felsen-L.	S. des rochers
S. saxifraga	Steinbrech L.	S. Saxifrage
S. vulgaris	Gemeines L.	S. enflé
SOLDANELLA	SOLDANELLA	SOLDANELLE
S. alpina	Alpenglockchen	S. des Alpes
S. minima	Zwerg-S.	S. naine
S. pusilla	Kleine-S.	Petite S.
SOLIDAGO	GOLDRUTE	SOLIDAGE
S. virga-aurea	Gemeine-G.	S. Vierge d'or
SPIRANTHES	WENDELAHRE	SPIRANTHE
S. aestivalis	Sommer-W.	S. d'été
S. autumnalis	Herbst-W.	S. d'automne
STACHYS	ZEIST	BÉTOINE
S. densiflora	Dichtblütiger-Z.	B. hérissée
STREPTOPUS	STREPTOPE	STREPTOPE
S. amplexifolius	Knotenfuss	S. à feuilles embrassantes
SWERTIA		SWERTIE
S. perennis	Moor-enzian	S. vivace
SYMPHYTUM	WALLWURZ	CONSOUDE
S. tuberosum	Knotige W.	C. tubéreuse
TETRAGONOLOBUS		TETRAGONOLOBE
T. maritimus	Spargelerbse	T. siliquex
TEUCRIUM	GAMANDER	GERMANDRÉE
T. chamaedrys	Heide G.	G. petit chêne
T. montanum	Berg-G.	G. des montagnes
THALICTRUM	WIESENRAUTE	PIGAMON
T. aquilegifolium	Akeleiblättrige W.	P. à feuilles d'Ancolie
THLASPI	TASCHELKRAUT	TABOURET
T. alpestre	Alpen-T.	T. des Alpes

T. corymbosum	Doldige T.	T. à fleurs en corymbe
T. perfoliatum	Durchwachsenblatt T.	T. perfolié
T. rotundifolium	Rundblättriges T.	T. à feuilles rondes
ssp. montanum	Berg-T.	T. des montagnes
THYMUS	THYMIAN	THYM
T. serpyllum	Feld-T.	T. serpolet
TOFIELDIA	LILIENSIMSE	TOFIELDIE
T. calyculata	Gemeine L.	T. à calicule
TOZZIA	TOZZIE	TOZZIE
T. alpina	Tozzie	T. des Alpes
TRAGOPOGON	BREKSBART	SALSAFIS
T. pratensis	Wiesen-B.	Salsafis des prés, Barbe de Bouc
TRIFOLIUM	KLEE	TRÈFLE
T. alpinum	Alpen-K.	T. des Alpes
T. arvense	Hasen-K.	T. des champs
T. badium	Braun-K.	T. brun
T. nivale	Schnee-K.	T. des neiges
T. thalii	Thals K.	T. de Thal
TROLLIUS	TROLLBLUME	TROLLE
T. europaeus	Trollblume	T. d'Europe
TULIPA	TULPE	TULIPE
T. australis	Südliche T.	T. méridionale
TUSSILAGO		
T. farfara	Huflattich	Pas-d'âne
VACCINIUM		AIRELLE
V. myrtillus	Heidelbeere	Myrtille
V. oxycoccus	Moosbeere	Canneberge à quatre pétales
V. uliginosum	Moorbeere	A. des marais
V. vitis-idaea	Preisselbeere	A. rouge
VALERIANA	BALDRIAN	VALÉRIANE
V. celtica	Penninischen B.	Nard, Spic celtique
V. dioica	Sumpf-B.	V. dioïque
V. montana	Berg-B.	V. des montagnes
V. saliunca	Felsschutt B.	V. Saliunca
V. saxatilis	Felsen-B.	V. des rochers
V. supina	Zwerg-B.	V. naine
V. tripteris	Dreischnittiger B.	V. trisequée
VERATRUM	GERMER	VÉRATRE
V. album	Weisser-G.	V. blanc
V. nigrum	Schwarzer-G.	V. noir
VERBASCUM	WOLLKRAUT	MOLÈNE
V. blattaria	Echtes Schabenkraut	M. Blattaire
V. chaixii	Chaix' W.	M. de Chaix
V. crassifolium	Berg-W.	M. à feuilles épaisses
V. lychnitis	Lampen-W.	M. Lychnite
V. nigrum	Dunkels-W.	M. noire
V. phlomoides	Filsiges W.	M. faux Plomis
V. pulverulentum	Flockiges-W.	M. pulvérulente
V. thapsiforme	Grossblütiges W.	Bonhomme
V. thapsus	Kleineblütiges W.	Bouillon blanc
VERONICA	EHRENPREIS	VÉRONIQUE
V. alpina	Alpen-E.	V. des Alpes
V. aphylla	Blattlöser E.	V. à tige nue
V. bellidioides	Rosetten-E.	V. Fausse Pâquerette
V. bonarota	Blaues Mänderle	V. de Buonarota
V. fruticans	Felsen-E.	V. des rochers
V. latifolia	Breitblättriger E.	V. à larges feuilles
V. lutea	Gelbes Mänderle	V. jaune
V. officinalis	Gebrauchlicher E.	V. officinale
V. spicata	Ahriger-E.	V. en épi
V. teucrium	Gamander artiger E.	V. Germandrée
VICIA	WICKE	VESCE
V. silvatica	Wald W.	V. des bois

VINCA	IMMERGRÜM	PERVENCHE
V. minor	Kleines I.	Petite P.
VINCETOXICUM		
V. officinale	Schwalbenwurz	Dompte-venin officinal
VIOLA	VEILCHEN	VIOLETTE
V. biflora	Zweiblütiges V.	V. à deux fleurs
V. calcarata	Langsporniges V.	V. éperonnée
V. cenisia	Mont Cenis V.	V. de Mont Cenis
V. dubyana	Dubys-V.	V. de Duby
V. lutea	Gelbes V.	V. jaune
V. palustris	Sumpf V.	V. des marais
V. pinnata	Fiederblättriges V.	V. pennée
V. rupestris	Sand-V.	V. des rocailles
V. tricolor	Acker-stiefmutterchen	V. tricolore
V. wolfiana	Wolfs V.	V. de Wolf

Index of Botanical Names

❋ indicates illustration. Synonyms are shown in *italics*

Index of English Names

※ indicates illustrations. * indicates names given by the author